# JUMP Math 2.1

**Book 2** Part 1 of 2

## Contents

jump math™

MULTIPLYING POTENTIAL.

**JUMP Math**
One Yonge Street, Suite 1014
Toronto, Ontario M5E 1E5
Canada
www.jumpmath.org

Writers: Dr. Francisco Kibedi, Dr. Anna Klebanov
Editors: Megan Burns, Liane Tsui, Julie Takasaki, Natalie Francis, Lindsay Karpenko, Susan Bindernagel, Jackie Dulson, Janice Dyer, Michelle MacAleese, Louise MacKenzie, Leanne Rancourt
Layout and Illustrations: Linh Lam, Fely Guinasao-Fernandes, Sawyer Paul
Cover Design: Blakeley Words+Pictures
Cover Photograph: © adriennexplores/Shutterstock

ISBN 978-1-928134-33-6

Third printing June 2019

Printed and bound in Canada

*A note to educators, parents, and everyone who believes that numeracy is as important as literacy for a fully functioning society*

# Welcome to JUMP Math

Entering the world of JUMP Math means believing that every child has the capacity to be fully numerate and to love math. Founder and mathematician John Mighton has used this premise to develop his innovative teaching method. The resulting resources isolate and describe concepts so clearly and incrementally that everyone can understand them.

JUMP Math is comprised of teacher's guides (which are the heart of our program), interactive whiteboard lessons, student assessment & practice books, evaluation materials, outreach programs, and teacher training. All of this is presented on the JUMP Math website: **www.jumpmath.org**.

Teacher's guides are available on the website for free use. Read the introduction to the teacher's guides before you begin using these resources. This will ensure that you understand both the philosophy and the methodology of JUMP Math. The assessment & practice books are designed for use by students, with adult guidance. Each student will have unique needs and it is important to provide the student with the appropriate support and encouragement as he or she works through the material.

Allow students to discover the concepts by themselves as much as possible. Mathematical discoveries can be made in small, incremental steps. The discovery of a new step is like untangling the parts of a puzzle. It is exciting and rewarding.

Students will need to answer the questions marked with a in a notebook. Grid paper notebooks should always be on hand for answering extra questions or when additional room for calculation is needed.

# Contents

# Unit 5: Geometry: 2-D Shapes

# Unit 6: Probability and Data Management: Sorting and Graphing

# Unit 7: Number Sense: Addition and Subtraction with Numbers to 100

# Unit 8: Geometry: Symmetry

# Unit 9: Number Sense: Equations and Word Problems

# Unit 10: Number Sense: Using 10 to Add and Subtract

# Unit 11: Measurement: More Length and Mass

## PART 2

# Unit 12: Number Sense: Skip Counting and Estimating

# Unit 13: Number Sense: Addition Strategies

# Unit 14: Number Sense: Subtraction Strategies

# Unit 15: Patterns and Algebra: Growing and Shrinking Patterns

# Unit 16: Geometry: 3-D Shapes

## Unit 17: Number Sense: Money

## Unit 18: Number Sense: Fractions, Multiplication, and Division

## Unit 19: Measurement: Time

# Unit 20: Probability and Data Management: Probability

# Unit 21: Measurement: Area, Calendars, Temperature, and Capacity

# Counting and Matching

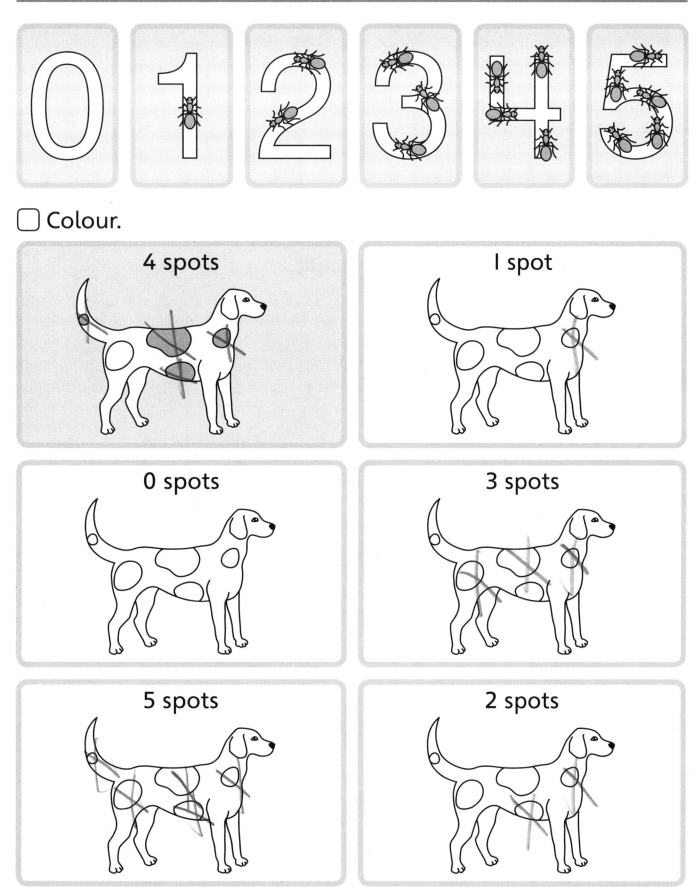

☐ Colour.

4 spots

1 spot

0 spots

3 spots

5 spots

2 spots

☐ Match by number.

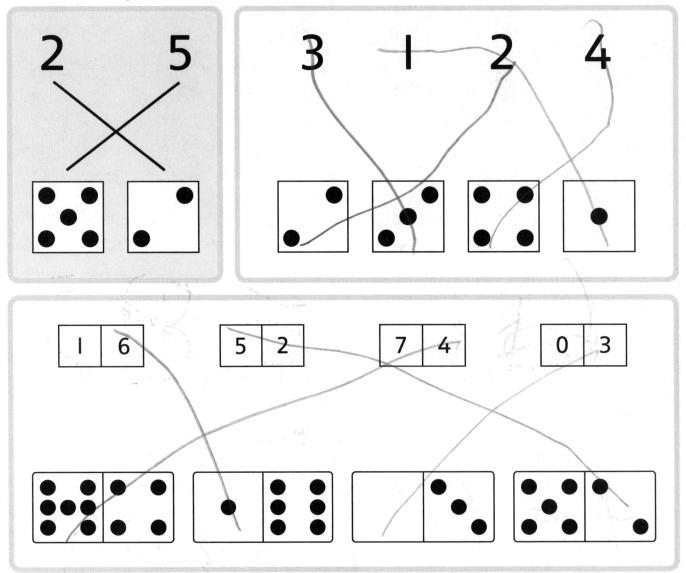

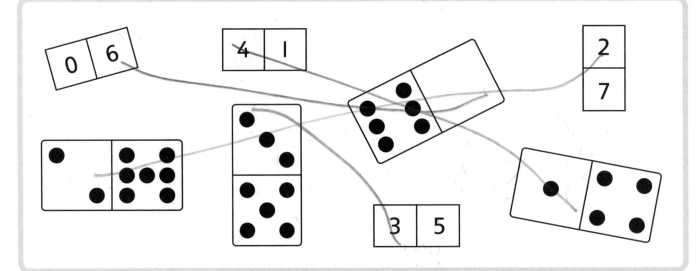

# One-to-One Correspondence

☐ Circle the one that is **more**.

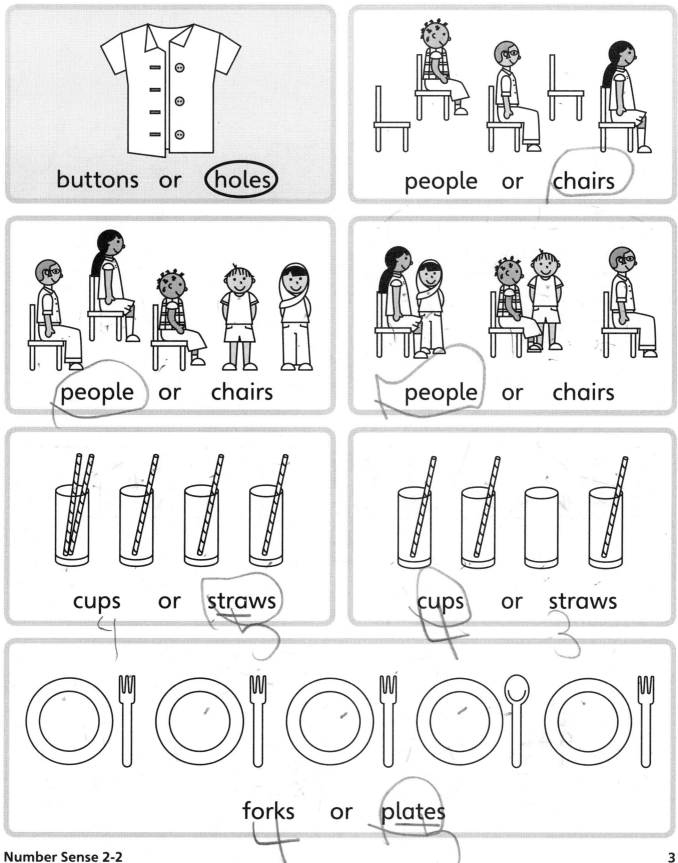

buttons or (holes)

people or (chairs)

(people) or chairs

people or chairs

cups or (straws)

cups or straws

forks or (plates)

☐ Pair them up to find out which is **more**.

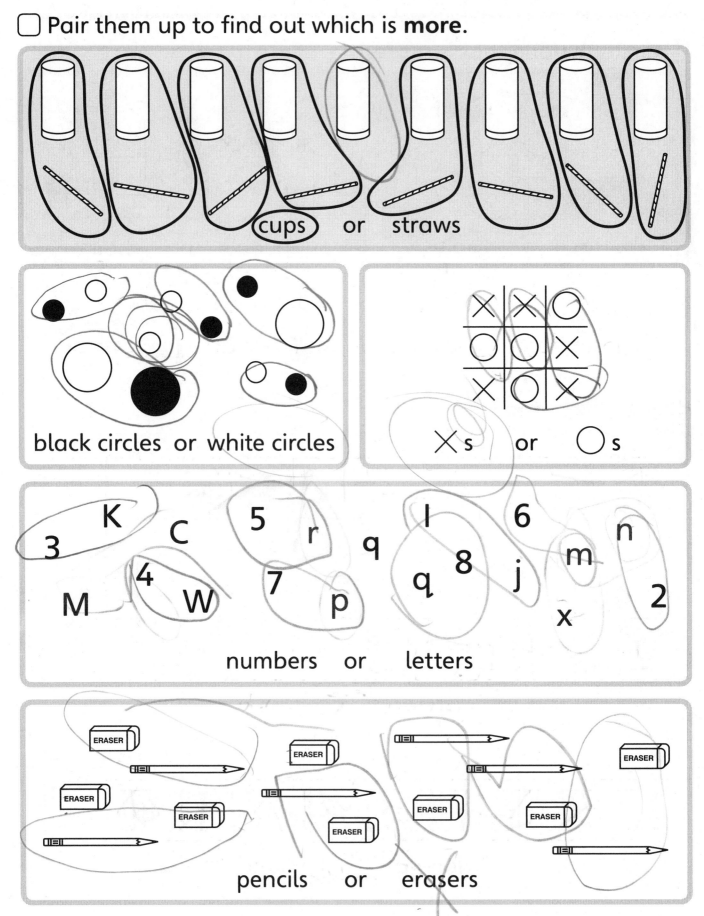

cups or straws

black circles or white circles

✕s or ◯s

K
3
C
5
r
q
l
6
n
M
4
W
7
p
8
q
j
m
x
2

numbers or letters

pencils or erasers

# More, Fewer, and Less

## How many ants?

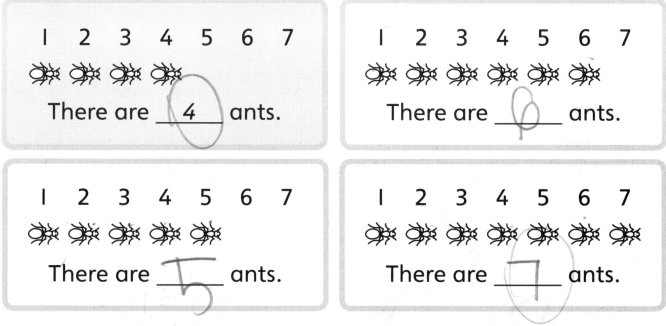

1  2  3  4  5  6  7

There are __4__ ants.

1  2  3  4  5  6  7

There are __6__ ants.

1  2  3  4  5  6  7

There are __5__ ants.

1  2  3  4  5  6  7

There are __7__ ants.

## How many blocks?

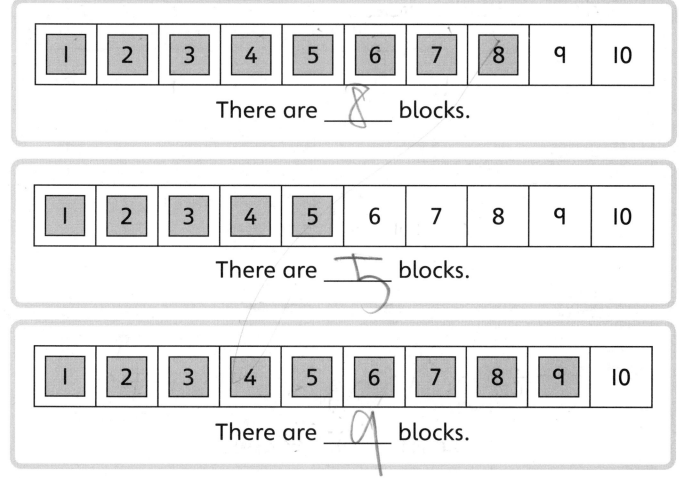

| 1 | 2 | 3 | 4 | 5 | 6 | 7 | 8 | 9 | 10 |

There are __8__ blocks.

| 1 | 2 | 3 | 4 | 5 | 6 | 7 | 8 | 9 | 10 |

There are __5__ blocks.

| 1 | 2 | 3 | 4 | 5 | 6 | 7 | 8 | 9 | 10 |

There are __9__ blocks.

- [ ] Trace the number of spiders.
- [ ] Trace the number of ants.
- [ ] Write **more**, **less**, or **fewer**.

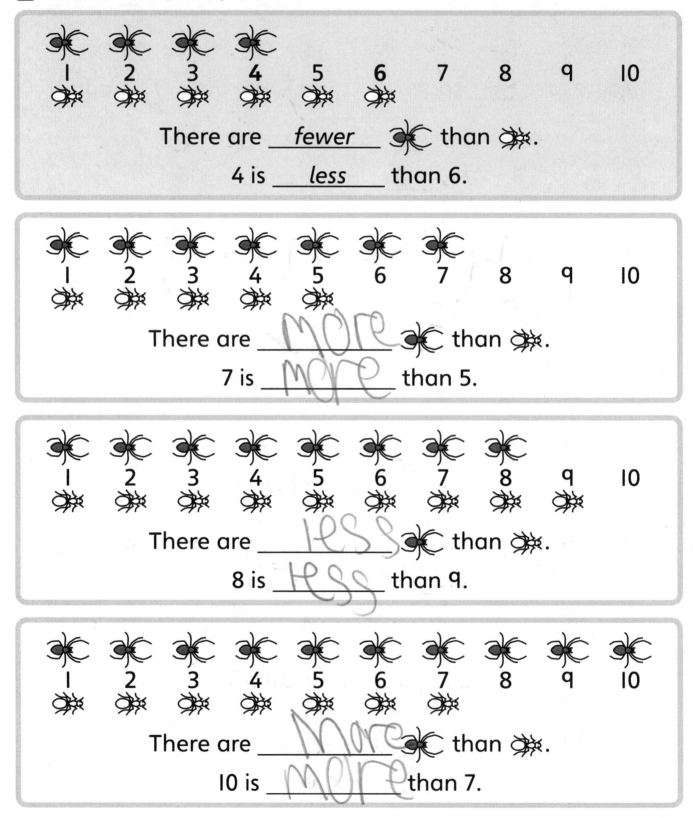

There are ___fewer___ 🕷 than 🐜.

4 is ___less___ than 6.

There are ___more___ 🕷 than 🐜.

7 is ___more___ than 5.

There are ___less___ 🕷 than 🐜.

8 is ___less___ than 9.

There are ___more___ 🕷 than 🐜.

10 is ___more___ than 7.

# How Many More?

☐ Circle the **extras**.
☐ Write how many more.

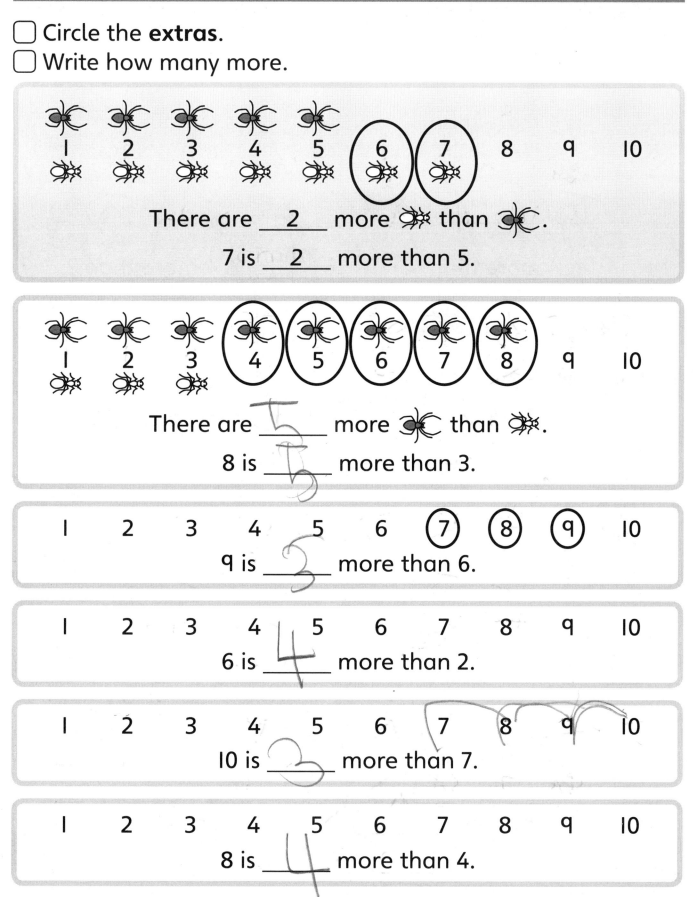

There are __2__ more 🕷 than 🐜.

7 is __2__ more than 5.

There are __5__ more 🕷 than 🐜.

8 is __5__ more than 3.

| 1 | 2 | 3 | 4 | 5 | 6 | ⑦ | ⑧ | ⑨ | 10 |

9 is __3__ more than 6.

| 1 | 2 | 3 | 4 | 5 | 6 | 7 | 8 | 9 | 10 |

6 is __4__ more than 2.

| 1 | 2 | 3 | 4 | 5 | 6 | 7 | 8 | 9 | 10 |

10 is __3__ more than 7.

| 1 | 2 | 3 | 4 | 5 | 6 | 7 | 8 | 9 | 10 |

8 is __4__ more than 4.

Write the extra numbers to find 4 more.

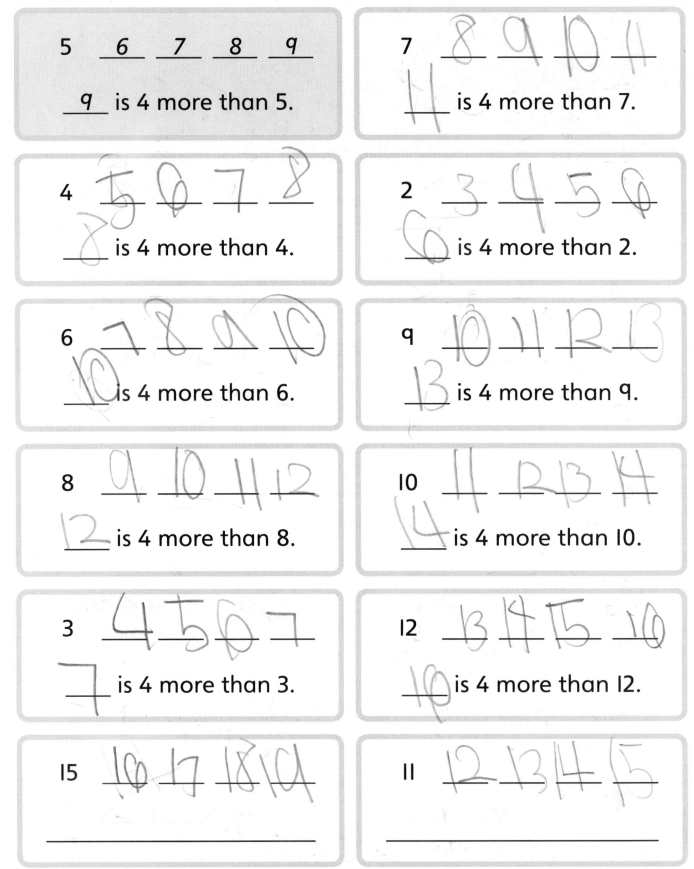

5 __6__ __7__ __8__ __9__

__9__ is 4 more than 5.

7 __8__ __9__ __10__ __11__

__11__ is 4 more than 7.

4 __5__ __6__ __7__ __8__

__8__ is 4 more than 4.

2 __3__ __4__ __5__ __6__

__6__ is 4 more than 2.

6 __7__ __8__ __9__ __10__

__10__ is 4 more than 6.

9 __10__ __11__ __12__ __13__

__13__ is 4 more than 9.

8 __9__ __10__ __11__ __12__

__12__ is 4 more than 8.

10 __11__ __12__ __13__ __14__

__14__ is 4 more than 10.

3 __4__ __5__ __6__ __7__

__7__ is 4 more than 3.

12 __13__ __14__ __15__ __16__

__16__ is 4 more than 12.

15 __16__ __17__ __18__ __19__

_____

11 __12__ __13__ __14__ __15__

_____

There are some apples in the bag.

How many apples altogether?

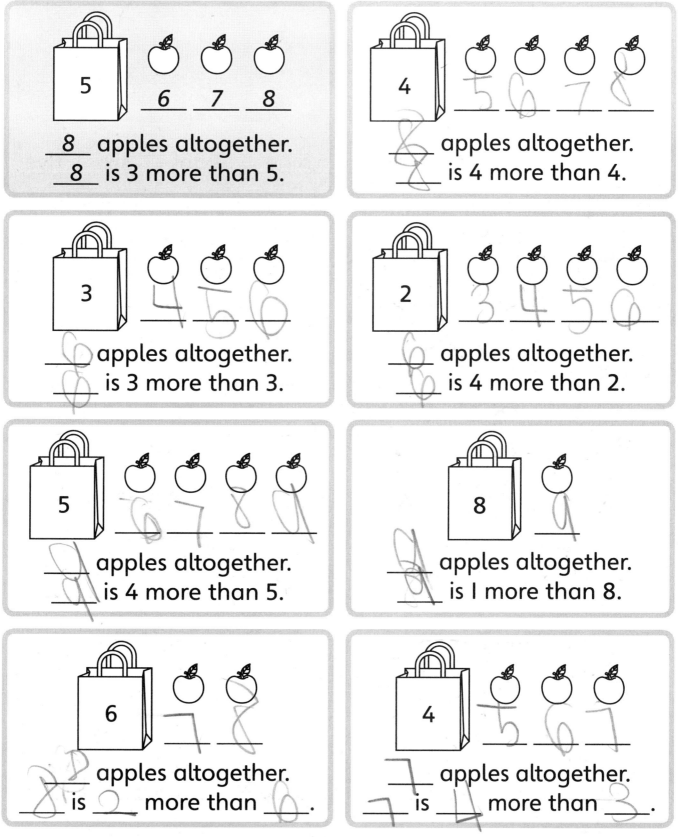

5 | 6 7 8
_8_ apples altogether.
_8_ is 3 more than 5.

4 | 5 6 7 8
_8_ apples altogether.
___ is 4 more than 4.

3 | 4 5 6
_6_ apples altogether.
___ is 3 more than 3.

2 | 3 4 5 6
_6_ apples altogether.
___ is 4 more than 2.

5 | 6 7 8 9
_9_ apples altogether.
___ is 4 more than 5.

8 | 9
_9_ apples altogether.
___ is 1 more than 8.

6 | 7 8
_8_ apples altogether.
___ is _2_ more than _6_.

4 | 5 6 7
_7_ apples altogether.
_7_ is _4_ more than _3_.

# Reading Number Words to Ten

☐ Match the numbers to the words.

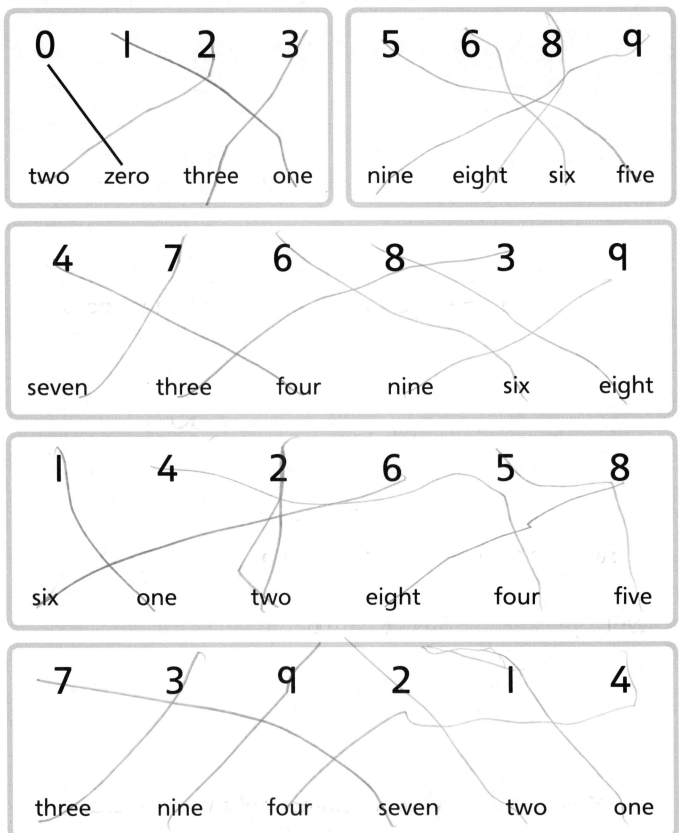

| 0 | 1 | 2 | 3 |
| --- | --- | --- | --- |
| two | zero | three | one |

| 5 | 6 | 8 | 9 |
| --- | --- | --- | --- |
| nine | eight | six | five |

| 4 | 7 | 6 | 8 | 3 | 9 |
| --- | --- | --- | --- | --- | --- |
| seven | three | four | nine | six | eight |

| 1 | 4 | 2 | 6 | 5 | 8 |
| --- | --- | --- | --- | --- | --- |
| six | one | two | eight | four | five |

| 7 | 3 | 9 | 2 | 1 | 4 |
| --- | --- | --- | --- | --- | --- |
| three | nine | four | seven | two | one |

☐ Write the numbers above the number words.

8          1

Eric has eight pencils and one eraser.

9          10

Alex is nine years old and Sam is ten years old.

7      2      0

Jane has seven crayons, two markers, and zero pens.

5          6

Ronin has five brothers and his sister has six brothers.

3      4

Cathy has three sisters and her brother has four sisters.

☐ Write your own sentence with a number word.

Dear AMMAR

Have a friend write the number above the word.

# Addition

☐ Add.

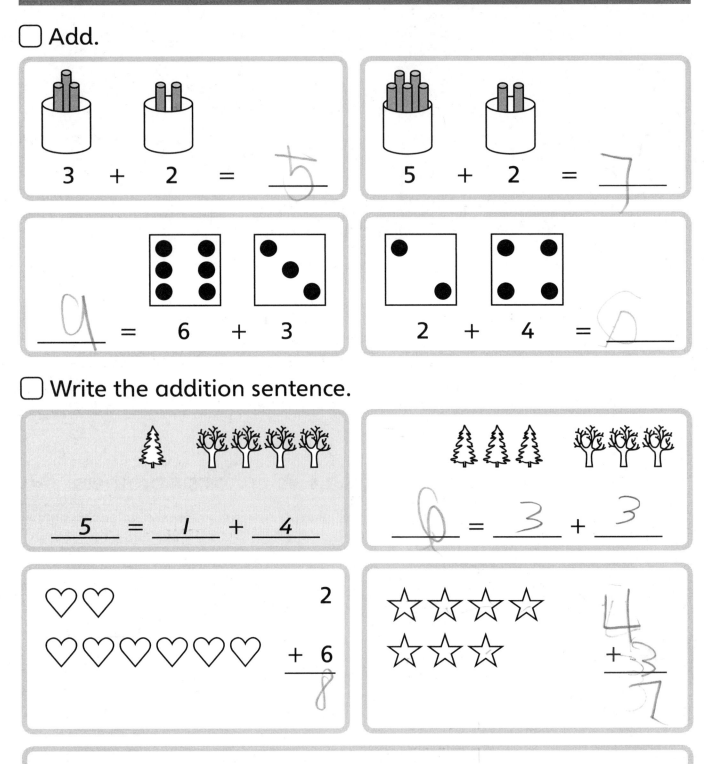

3 + 2 = _5_

5 + 2 = _7_

_9_ = 6 + 3

2 + 4 = _6_

☐ Write the addition sentence.

_5_ = _1_ + _4_

_6_ = _3_ + _3_

2
+ 6
___
_8_

_4_
+ _3_
___

_2_ + _5_ + _1_ = _8_

## Draw dots to add.

3 + 2 + 4 = _9_

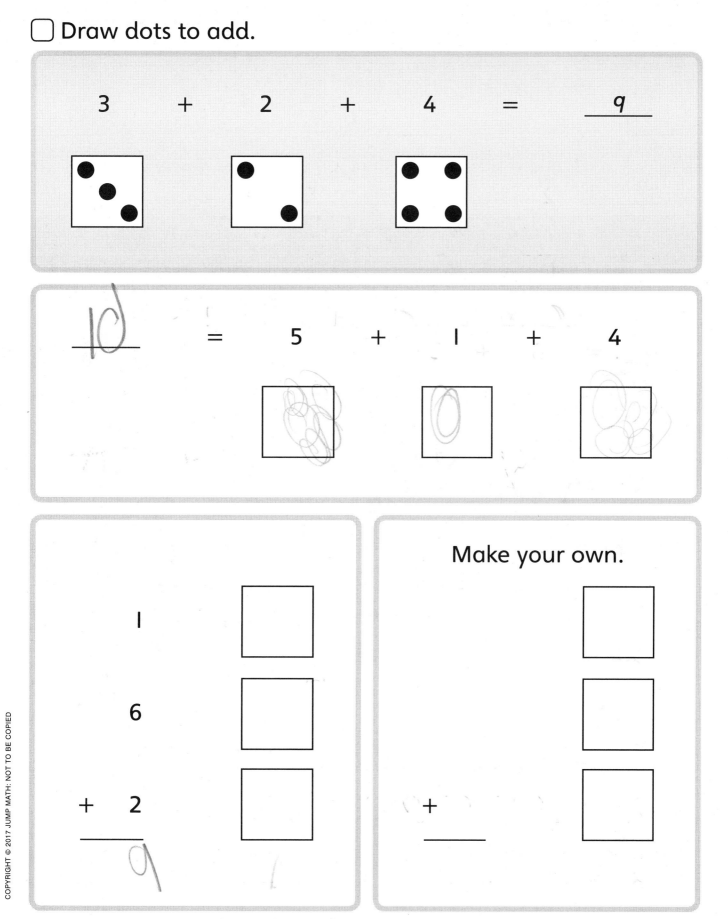

_10_ = 5 + 1 + 4

1

6

+ 2
___
_9_

Make your own.

+
___

# Subtraction

☐ Subtract.

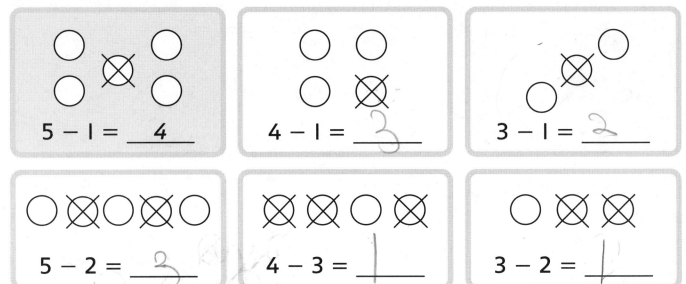

5 − 1 = ___4___     4 − 1 = ___3___     3 − 1 = ___2___

5 − 2 = ___3___     4 − 3 = ___1___     3 − 2 = ___1___

Braden takes away the black hearts.
How many are left?

3 − 1 = ___2___     6 − 1 = ___5___     4 − 2 = ___2___

5 − 3 = ___2___     5 − 4 = ___1___     4 − 3 = ___1___

☐ Write a subtraction sentence for the picture.

5 − 1 = 4          4 − 3 = 1          5 − 2 = 3

## ☐ Cross out the circles and subtract.

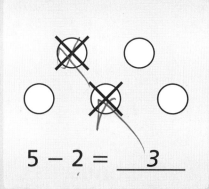

$5 - 2 = \underline{\quad 3 \quad}$

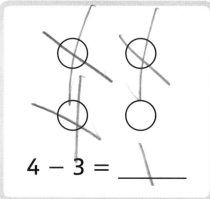

$4 - 3 = \underline{\quad 1 \quad}$

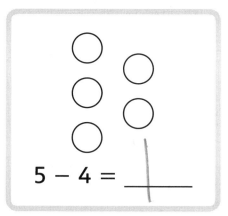

$5 - 4 = \underline{\quad 1 \quad}$

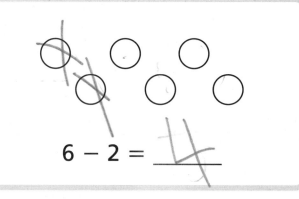

$6 - 2 = \underline{\quad 4 \quad}$

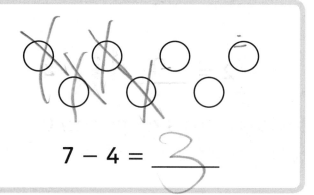

$7 - 4 = \underline{\quad 3 \quad}$

## ☐ Draw a picture to subtract.

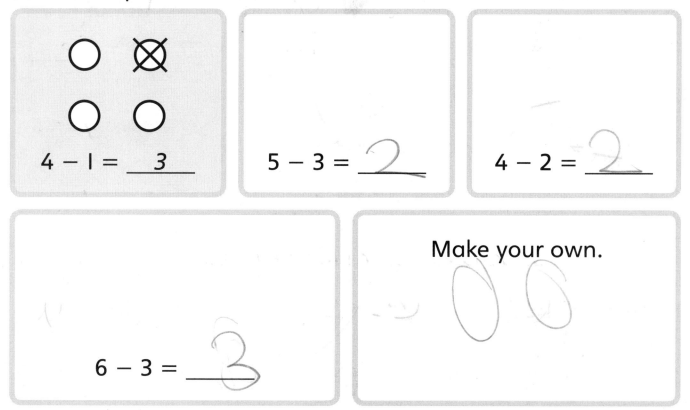

$4 - 1 = \underline{\quad 3 \quad}$

$5 - 3 = \underline{\quad 2 \quad}$

$4 - 2 = \underline{\quad 2 \quad}$

$6 - 3 = \underline{\quad 3 \quad}$

Make your own.

# Adding and Subtracting 0

☐ Add 0 dots.

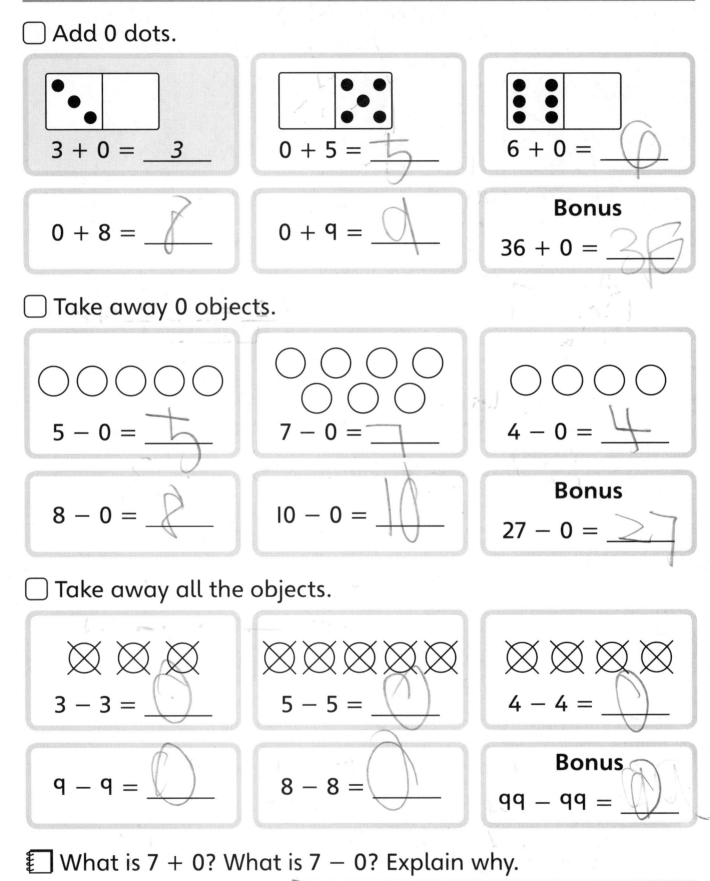

$3 + 0 = \underline{\quad 3 \quad}$

$0 + 5 = \underline{\quad 5 \quad}$

$6 + 0 = \underline{\quad 6 \quad}$

$0 + 8 = \underline{\quad 8 \quad}$

$0 + 9 = \underline{\quad 9 \quad}$

**Bonus**

$36 + 0 = \underline{\quad 36 \quad}$

☐ Take away 0 objects.

$5 - 0 = \underline{\quad 5 \quad}$

$7 - 0 = \underline{\quad 7 \quad}$

$4 - 0 = \underline{\quad 4 \quad}$

$8 - 0 = \underline{\quad 8 \quad}$

$10 - 0 = \underline{\quad 10 \quad}$

**Bonus**

$27 - 0 = \underline{\quad 27 \quad}$

☐ Take away all the objects.

$3 - 3 = \underline{\quad 0 \quad}$

$5 - 5 = \underline{\quad 0 \quad}$

$4 - 4 = \underline{\quad 0 \quad}$

$9 - 9 = \underline{\quad 0 \quad}$

$8 - 8 = \underline{\quad 0 \quad}$

**Bonus**

$99 - 99 = \underline{\quad 0 \quad}$

☐ What is $7 + 0$? What is $7 - 0$? Explain why.

# Counting to 20

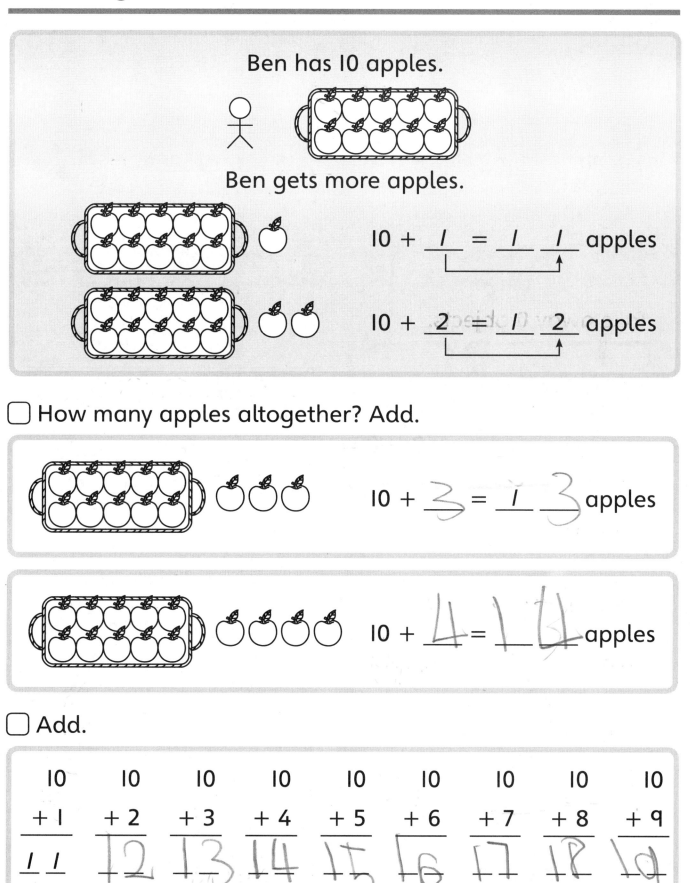

Ben has 10 apples.

Ben gets more apples.

10 + __1__ = __1__ __1__ apples

10 + __2__ = __1__ __2__ apples

☐ How many apples altogether? Add.

10 + __3__ = __1__ __3__ apples

10 + __4__ = __1__ __4__ apples

☐ Add.

| 10 | 10 | 10 | 10 | 10 | 10 | 10 | 10 | 10 |
|----|----|----|----|----|----|----|----|----|
| + 1 | + 2 | + 3 | + 4 | + 5 | + 6 | + 7 | + 8 | + 9 |
| 1 1 | 12 | 13 | 14 | 15 | 16 | 17 | 18 | 19 |

# How many?

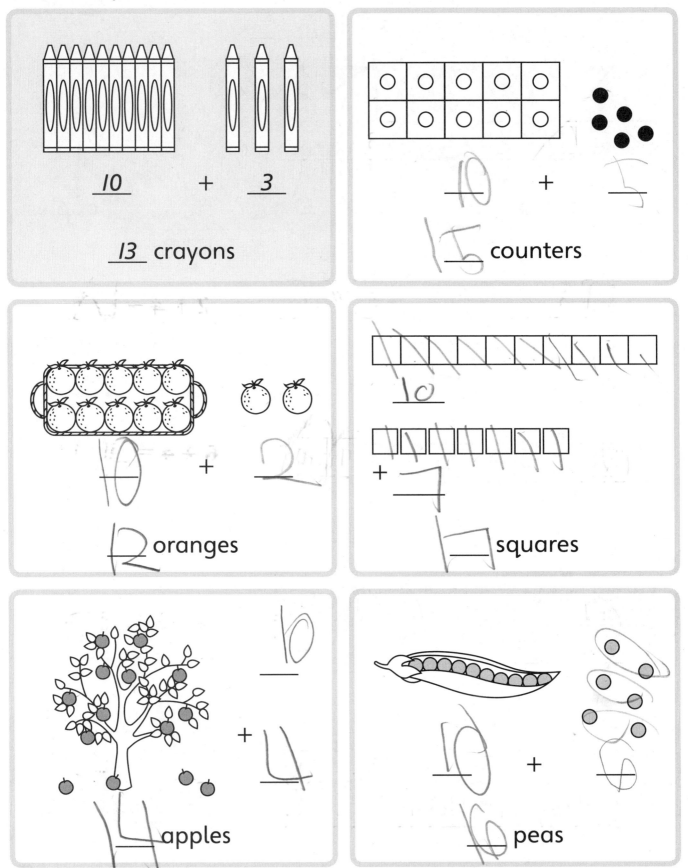

__10__ + __3__

__13__ crayons

____ + ____

_15_ counters

____ + ____

_12_ oranges

_10_

+ _7_

____ squares

_10_

+ _4_

_14_ apples

_10_ + ____

_16_ peas

# Adding Using a Chart

☐ Circle the next 4 squares.
☐ Add.

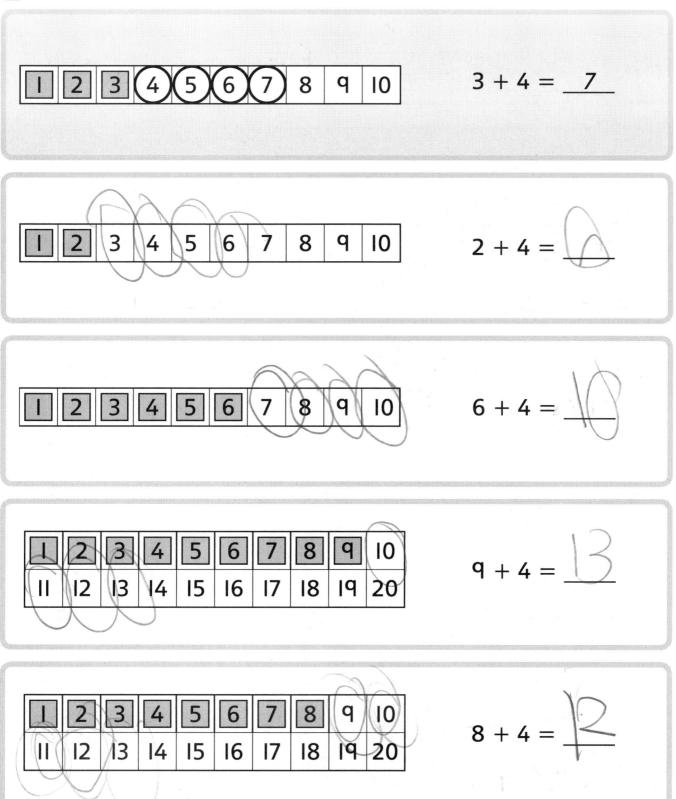

| 1 | 2 | 3 | 4 | 5 | 6 | 7 | 8 | 9 | 10 |

3 + 4 = __7__

| 1 | 2 | 3 | 4 | 5 | 6 | 7 | 8 | 9 | 10 |

2 + 4 = __6__

| 1 | 2 | 3 | 4 | 5 | 6 | 7 | 8 | 9 | 10 |

6 + 4 = __10__

| 1 | 2 | 3 | 4 | 5 | 6 | 7 | 8 | 9 | 10 |
| 11 | 12 | 13 | 14 | 15 | 16 | 17 | 18 | 19 | 20 |

9 + 4 = __13__

| 1 | 2 | 3 | 4 | 5 | 6 | 7 | 8 | 9 | 10 |
| 11 | 12 | 13 | 14 | 15 | 16 | 17 | 18 | 19 | 20 |

8 + 4 = __12__

☐ Shade the first number of squares.
☐ Circle the second number of squares.
☐ Add.

| 1 | 2 | 3 | 4 | 5 | 6 | 7 | 8 | 9 | 10 |
|---|---|---|---|---|---|---|---|---|---|
| 11 | 12 | 13 | 14 | 15 | 16 | 17 | 18 | 19 | 20 |

$7 + 6 =$ __13__

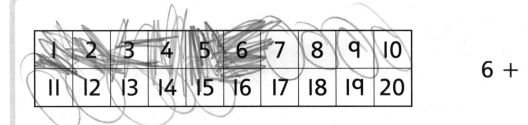

$6 + 9 =$ __15__

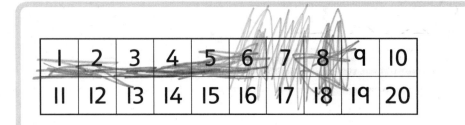

$8 + 8 =$ __16__

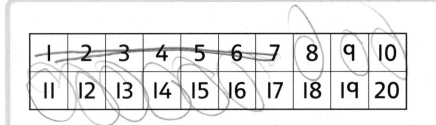

$7 + 9 =$ __16__

| 1 | 2 | 3 | 4 | 5 | 6 | 7 | 8 | 9 | 10 |
|---|---|---|---|---|---|---|---|---|---|
| 11 | 12 | 13 | 14 | 15 | 16 | 17 | 18 | 19 | 20 |

$9 + 4 =$ __13__

Tina pretends the first number of squares are shaded.
Then she circles the second number of squares.

| 1 | 2 | 3 | 4 | ⑤ | ⑥ | ⑦ | 8 | 9 | 10 |

$4 + 3 = \underline{\phantom{x}7\phantom{x}}$

☐ Use Tina's way to add.

| 1 | 2 | 3 | 4 | 5 | ⑥ | ⑦ | 8 | 9 | 10 |

$5 + 2 = \underline{7}$

| ~~1~~ | ~~2~~ | ~~3~~ | ④ | ⑤ | ⑥ | ⑦ | ⑧ | ⑨ | 10 |

$3 + 6 = \underline{9}$

| ~~1~~ | ~~2~~ | ~~3~~ | ~~4~~ | ⑤ | ⑥ | 7 | 8 | 9 | 10 |

$4 + 2 = \underline{6}$

| 1 | 2 | 3 | 4 | 5 | 6 | 7 | 8 | 9 | 10 |

$5 + 3 = \underline{8}$

| 1 | 2 | 3 | 4 | 5 | 6 | 7 | ⑧ | 9 | ⑩ |
|---|---|---|---|---|---|---|---|---|----|
| 11 | 12 | 13 | 14 | 15 | 16 | 17 | 18 | 19 | 20 |

$7 + 5 = \underline{12}$

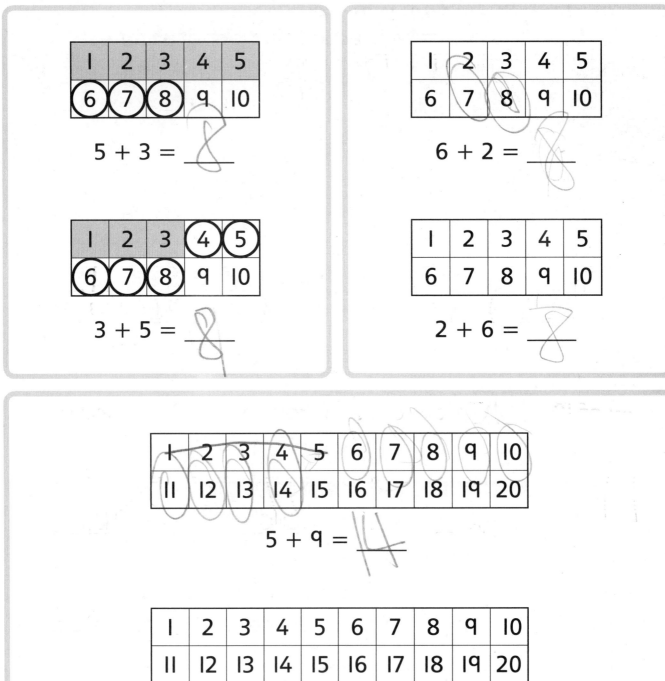

5 + 3 = 8

3 + 5 = 8

6 + 2 = 8

2 + 6 = 8

5 + 9 = 14

9 + 5 = 14

What do you notice? _5+3_____

# Tens and Ones Blocks

One row of 10 and how many more ones?

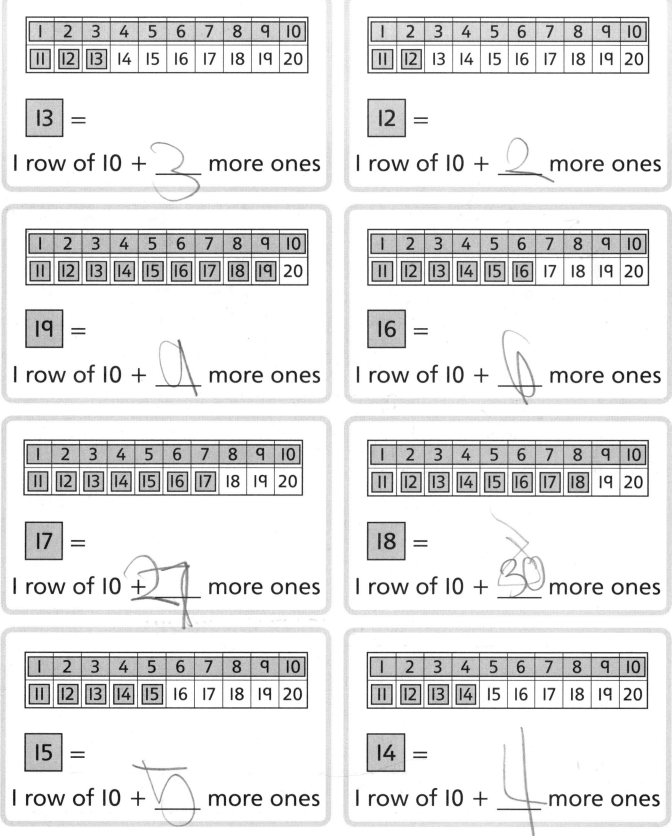

| 1 | 2 | 3 | 4 | 5 | 6 | 7 | 8 | 9 | 10 |
|---|---|---|---|---|---|---|---|---|----|
| 11 | 12 | 13 | 14 | 15 | 16 | 17 | 18 | 19 | 20 |

13 =

1 row of 10 + __3__ more ones

| 1 | 2 | 3 | 4 | 5 | 6 | 7 | 8 | 9 | 10 |
|---|---|---|---|---|---|---|---|---|----|
| 11 | 12 | 13 | 14 | 15 | 16 | 17 | 18 | 19 | 20 |

12 =

1 row of 10 + __2__ more ones

| 1 | 2 | 3 | 4 | 5 | 6 | 7 | 8 | 9 | 10 |
|---|---|---|---|---|---|---|---|---|----|
| 11 | 12 | 13 | 14 | 15 | 16 | 17 | 18 | 19 | 20 |

19 =

1 row of 10 + __9__ more ones

| 1 | 2 | 3 | 4 | 5 | 6 | 7 | 8 | 9 | 10 |
|---|---|---|---|---|---|---|---|---|----|
| 11 | 12 | 13 | 14 | 15 | 16 | 17 | 18 | 19 | 20 |

16 =

1 row of 10 + __6__ more ones

| 1 | 2 | 3 | 4 | 5 | 6 | 7 | 8 | 9 | 10 |
|---|---|---|---|---|---|---|---|---|----|
| 11 | 12 | 13 | 14 | 15 | 16 | 17 | 18 | 19 | 20 |

17 =

1 row of 10 + __7__ more ones

| 1 | 2 | 3 | 4 | 5 | 6 | 7 | 8 | 9 | 10 |
|---|---|---|---|---|---|---|---|---|----|
| 11 | 12 | 13 | 14 | 15 | 16 | 17 | 18 | 19 | 20 |

18 =

1 row of 10 + __8__ more ones

| 1 | 2 | 3 | 4 | 5 | 6 | 7 | 8 | 9 | 10 |
|---|---|---|---|---|---|---|---|---|----|
| 11 | 12 | 13 | 14 | 15 | 16 | 17 | 18 | 19 | 20 |

15 =

1 row of 10 + __5__ more ones

| 1 | 2 | 3 | 4 | 5 | 6 | 7 | 8 | 9 | 10 |
|---|---|---|---|---|---|---|---|---|----|
| 11 | 12 | 13 | 14 | 15 | 16 | 17 | 18 | 19 | 20 |

14 =

1 row of 10 + __4__ more ones

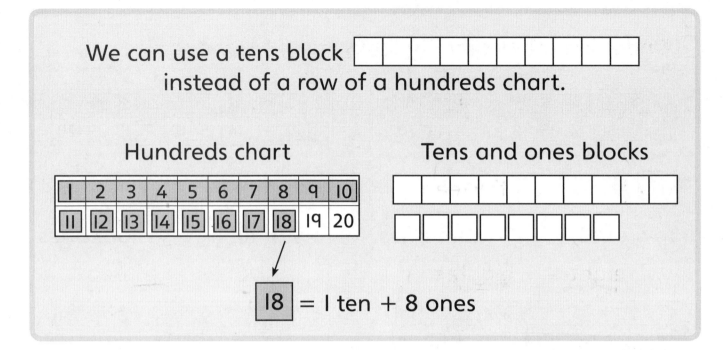

We can use a tens block [        ] instead of a row of a hundreds chart.

Hundreds chart

| 1 | 2 | 3 | 4 | 5 | 6 | 7 | 8 | 9 | 10 |
|---|---|---|---|---|---|---|---|---|---|
| 11 | 12 | 13 | 14 | 15 | 16 | 17 | 18 | 19 | 20 |

Tens and ones blocks

18 = 1 ten + 8 ones

## What number do the blocks show?

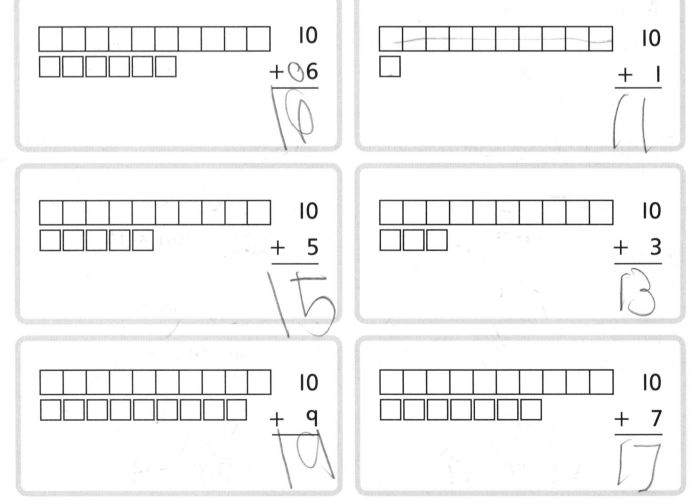

10
+ 6
16

10
+ 1
11

10
+ 5
15

10
+ 3
13

10
+ 9
19

10
+ 7
17

# Reading Number Words to Twenty

☐ Underline the beginning letters that are the same.

| | |
|---|---|
| <u>six</u>        <u>six</u>teen | two        twelve |
| three        thirteen | <u>four</u>        <u>four</u>teen |
| eight        eighteen | five        fifteen |

☐ Circle the digits that are the same.

| | | |
|---|---|---|
| 1②        1② | 16        16 | 17        17 |
| 9        19 | 8        18 | 3        13 |

☐ Underline and circle the same parts.

| | |
|---|---|
| <u>three</u> =③<br><u>thi</u>rteen = 1③ | <u>four</u> = 4<br><u>four</u>teen = 14 |
| <u>five</u> = 5<br><u>fif</u>teen = 15 | <u>nine</u> = 9<br><u>nine</u>teen = 19 |
| <u>seven</u> = 7<br><u>seven</u>teen = 17 | <u>two</u> = 2<br><u>twe</u>lve = 12 |

☐ Write the number.

**th**irteen = _1_ _3_    **seven**teen = _17_    **fif**teen = _15_

sixteen = _16_    fourteen = _14_    twelve = _12_

nineteen = _19_    eighteen = _18_    eleven = _11_

☐ Match the word with the number.

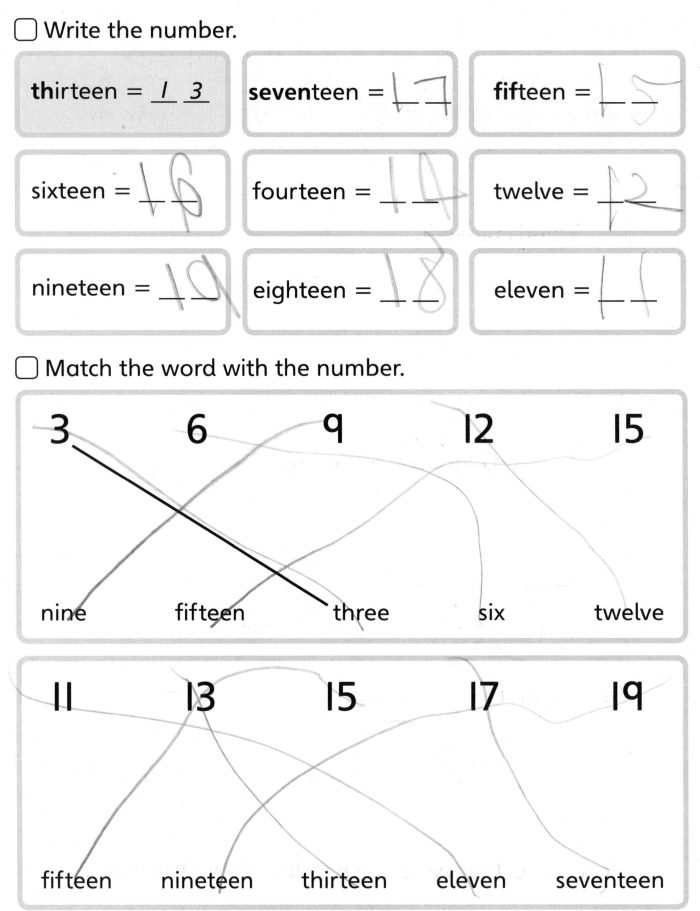

3          6          9          12          15

nine      fifteen      three      six      twelve

11          13          15          17          19

fifteen      nineteen      thirteen      eleven      seventeen

☐ Write the number above the number word.

| | |
|---|---|
| 13<br>Ella is thirteen months old. | *20*<br>Marcel has twenty teeth. |
| *10*<br>Sixteen friends played tag. | *11*<br>Holidays start in eleven days. |

*15*
We played basketball for fifteen minutes.

*18*
Cody invited eighteen friends to his birthday party.

**Bonus**
*12*
Amy's soccer team has twelve players —
*7*     *5*
seven girls and five boys.

☐ Write your own sentence with a number word.

*OM has 3three stuff*

Have a partner write the number above the word.

*fourteen*

# Writing Number Words to Twenty

☐ Answer the question using both the number and the word.

What grade are you in? __2__ = ___two___

How many letters are in your first name? __2__ = __two__

How old are you? __8__ = __eight__

How many pets do you have? __0__ = __zero__

How many girls are in your class? __3__ = __two__

How many boys are in your class? __4__ = __eleven__

How many months are in a year? __12__ = __twelve__

How many blank lines (__) are on this page? __4__ = __four__

**Bonus**

How many letters are always consonants? __21__ = _____

a b c d e f g h i j k l m n o p q r s t u v w x y z

# First Word Problems

☐ Add using the pictures.

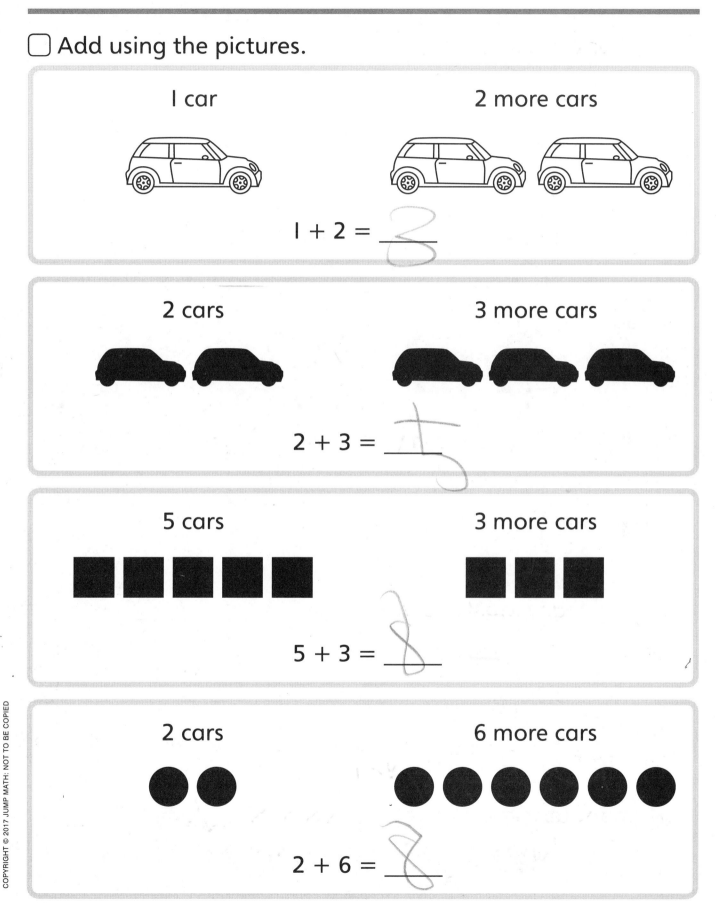

1 car            2 more cars

$1 + 2 = \underline{3}$

2 cars            3 more cars

$2 + 3 = \underline{5}$

5 cars            3 more cars

$5 + 3 = \underline{8}$

2 cars            6 more cars

$2 + 6 = \underline{8}$

☐ Write the numbers above the number words.
☐ Draw counters to show the numbers.
☐ Write the number sentence.
☐ Write the answer as a word.

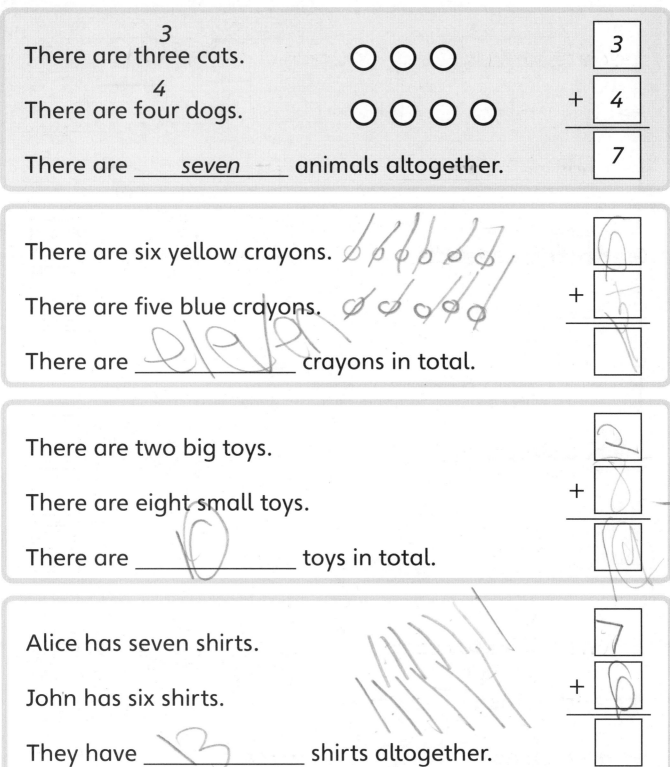

*3*
There are three cats. ○ ○ ○

*4*
There are four dogs. ○ ○ ○ ○

There are ___seven___ animals altogether.

| 3 |
|---|
| + 4 |
| 7 |

There are six yellow crayons.

There are five blue crayons.

There are __eleven__ crayons in total.

There are two big toys.

There are eight small toys.

There are __10__ toys in total.

Alice has seven shirts.

John has six shirts.

They have __13__ shirts altogether.

☐ Write the numbers above the number words.
☐ Draw circles and cross some out to subtract.
☐ Write the subtraction sentence.
☐ Write the answer as a word.

8
Jack had eight crayons.    ⊗⊗⊗○○○○○    | 8 |

3
He gave three to his sister.    − | 3 |

Jack has _____ *five* _____ crayons left.    | 5 |

---

Glen had four pencils.    | 4 |

He lost one of them.    − | 1 |

Glen has _____ Three _____ pencils left.    | 3 |

---

Lily had six marbles.    | 6 |

She gave two to Kate.    − | 2 |

Lily has _____ FOUR _____ marbles left.    | 4 |

---

Simon had five toy cars.    | 5 |

His teacher took three of them.    − | 3 |

Now Simon has _____ two _____ toy cars.    | 2 |

# Making Word Problems

What are you adding together?

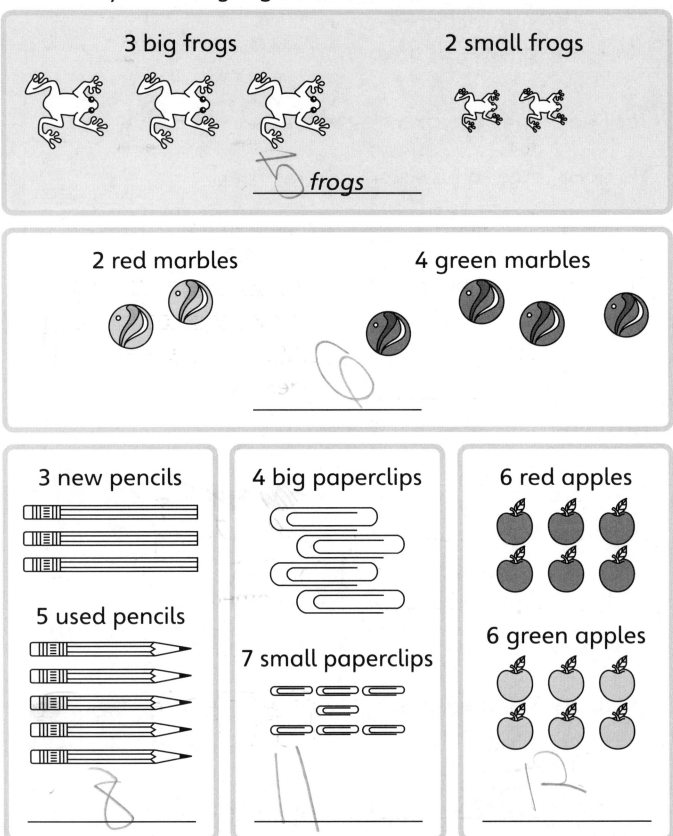

3 big frogs          2 small frogs

_____5_____ frogs

2 red marbles          4 green marbles

_____

3 new pencils

5 used pencils

_____

4 big paperclips

7 small paperclips

_____

6 red apples

6 green apples

_____

☐ Add.
☐ Write what you are adding.

There are 5 big frogs.

There are 2 small frogs.

There are __7__ ___frogs___ altogether.

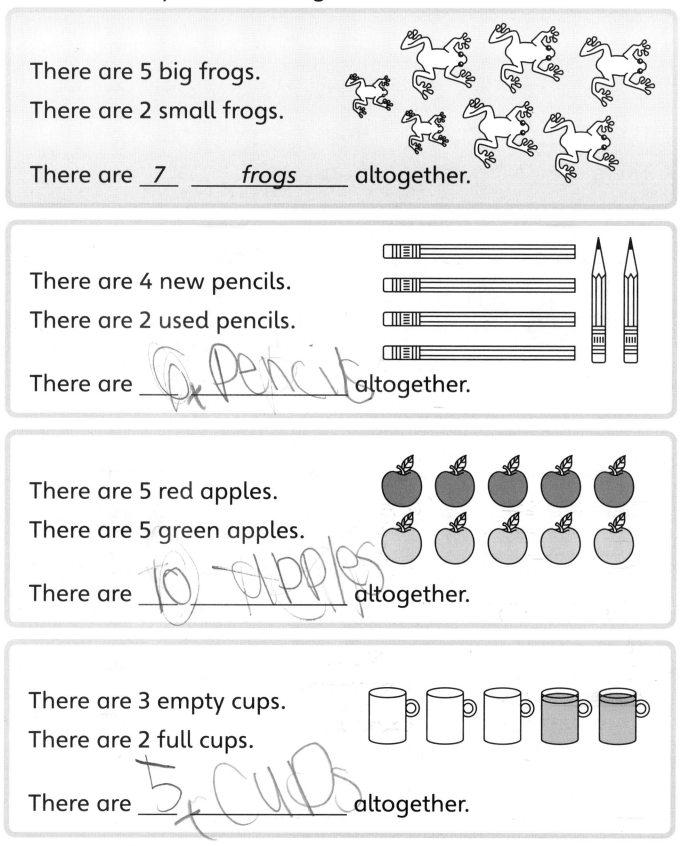

There are 4 new pencils.

There are 2 used pencils.

There are __6 Pencils__ altogether.

There are 5 red apples.

There are 5 green apples.

There are __10 apples__ altogether.

There are 3 empty cups.

There are 2 full cups.

There are __5 cups__ altogether.

☐ Use the words to make a problem for each picture.

~~big~~          ~~small~~          ~~empty~~          ~~full~~
farm          zoo          happy          sad

There are __3__   __big__   frogs.
There are __2__   __small__   frogs.

There are __5__ frogs altogether.

There are _3, empty_ bowls.
There are _2, full_ bowls.

There are __5__ bowls altogether.

There are __2__ _few_ animals.
There are __3__ _7_ animals.

There are __5__ animals altogether.

There are __4__ _four_ faces.
There are __3__ _three_ faces.

There are __7__ faces altogether.

☐ Write a question that matches Rani's answer.
☐ Finish her answer.

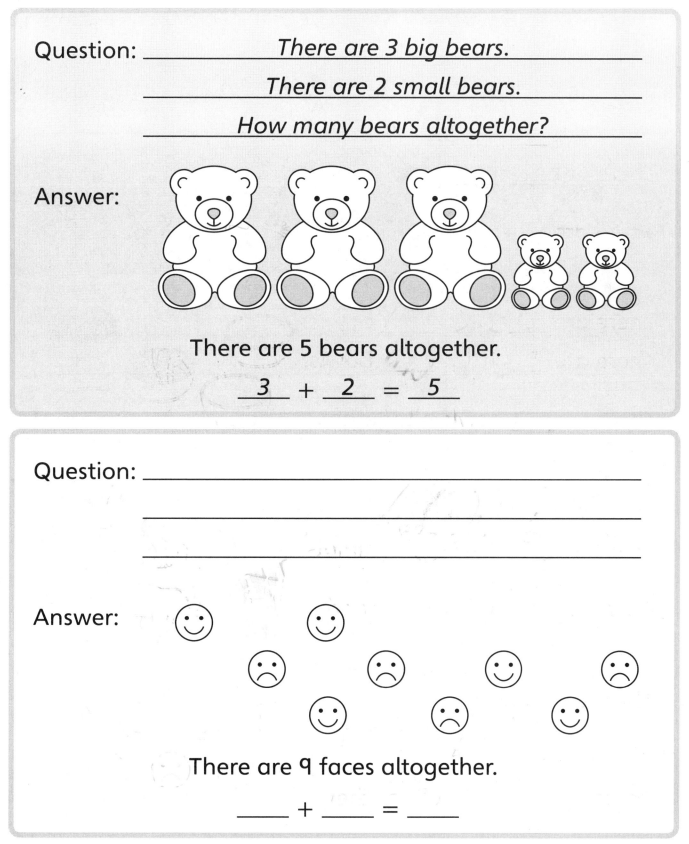

Question: _____ *There are 3 big bears.* _____

_____ *There are 2 small bears.* _____

_____ *How many bears altogether?* _____

Answer:

There are 5 bears altogether.

__3__ + __2__ = __5__

Question: _____

_____

_____

Answer:

There are 9 faces altogether.

_____ + _____ = _____

☐ Write a problem for the picture.
☐ Write the subtraction sentence.

There are 10 flies.

The frog eats 3 of them.

How many are left?

$\underline{10} - \underline{3} = \underline{7}$

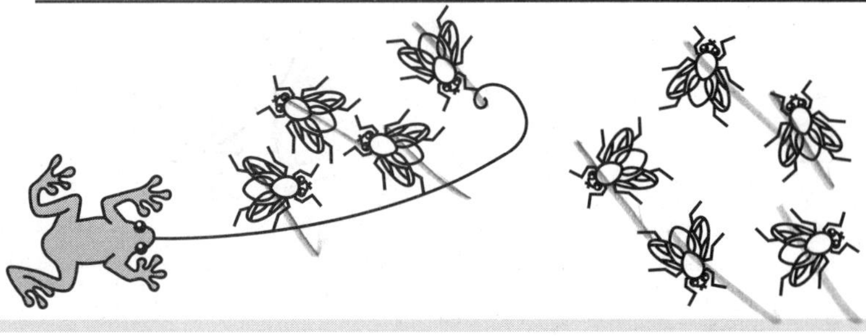

$9 - 4 = 5$

$9 - 2 = 7$

☐ Write a problem for the picture.
☐ Write the subtraction sentence.

There were 9 apples in the tree.

4 of them fell.

How many are left?

9 - 4 = 5

_____

_____

_____

9 - 2 = 4

_____

_____

_____

7 - 3 = 4

# Ordinal Numbers

☐ Circle the **first** 3 pencils.
☐ Colour the **3rd** pencil.
☐ Cross out the **last** eraser.

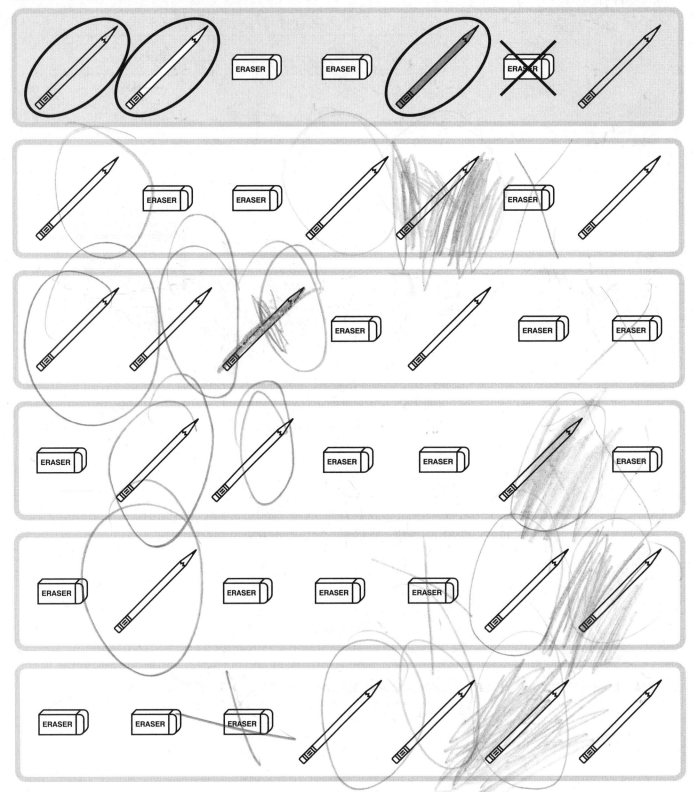

☐ Check ✓ the first one.
☐ Circle the answer.

Who is 3rd?

Who is 7th?

SCHOOL BUS
STOP

Which dog is 6th?

Which train car is 8th?

# Writing Ordinals

☐ Finish writing the ordinal.

| first = 1 _st_ | second = 2 _nd_ | third = 3 _rd_ |
| fourth = 4 _th_ | fifth = 5 _th_ | sixth = 6 _th_ |
| seventh = 7 _th_ | eighth = 8 _th_ | ninth = 9 _th_ |

☐ Write the ordinal.

| seventh = _7th_ | third = _3rd_ |
| tenth = _10th_ | first = _1st_ |
| fourth = _4th_ | second = _2nd_ |
| fifth = _5th_ | ninth = _9th_ |

☐ Finish writing the ordinals.

8 _th_    3 _rd_    4 _th_    9 _th_    2 _nd_

6 _th_    1 _st_    10 _th_    5 _th_    7 _th_

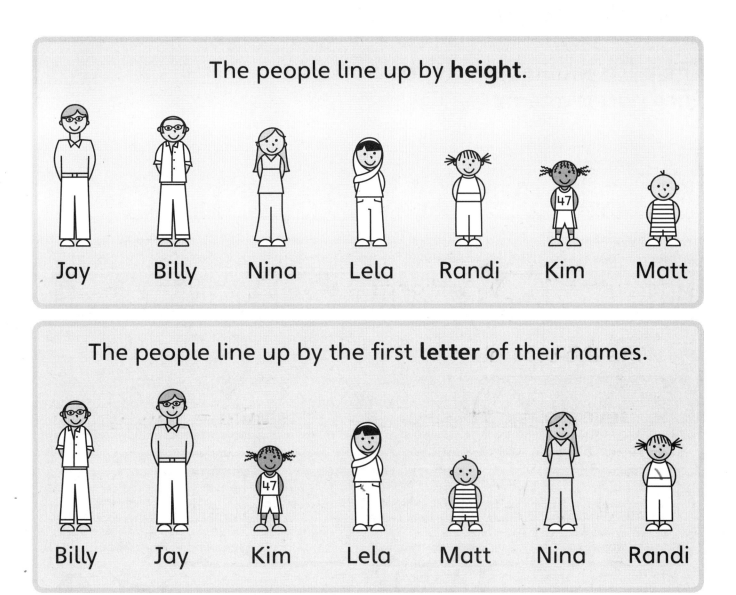

The people line up by **height**.

Jay    Billy    Nina    Lela    Randi    Kim    Matt

The people line up by the first **letter** of their names.

Billy    Jay    Kim    Lela    Matt    Nina    Randi

☐ Use the pictures to fill in the blanks.

Nina is ___*3rd*___ in the **height** line.

Nina is ___6th___ in the **letter** line.

Nina is closer to the front of the ___height___ line.

Kim is closer to the front of the ___letter___ line.

___Lela___ is in the same place in both lines.

Matt is the last person in the ___height___ line.

Billy is the first person in the ___height___ line.

# Cores of Patterns

The parts that repeat are the **core**.
Each part is a **term**.

☐ Circle the core.

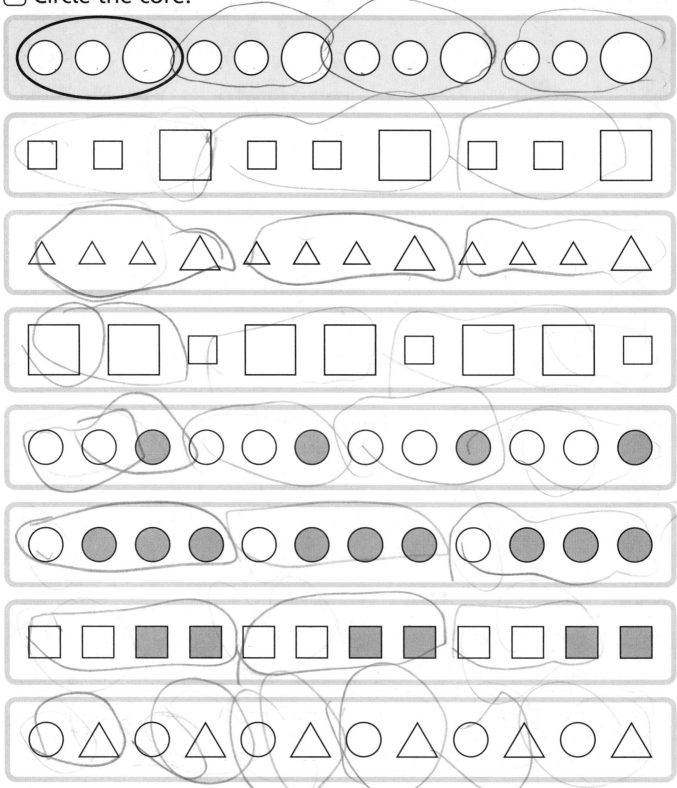

**Patterns and Algebra 2-1**

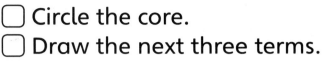

Circle the core.

Draw the next three terms.

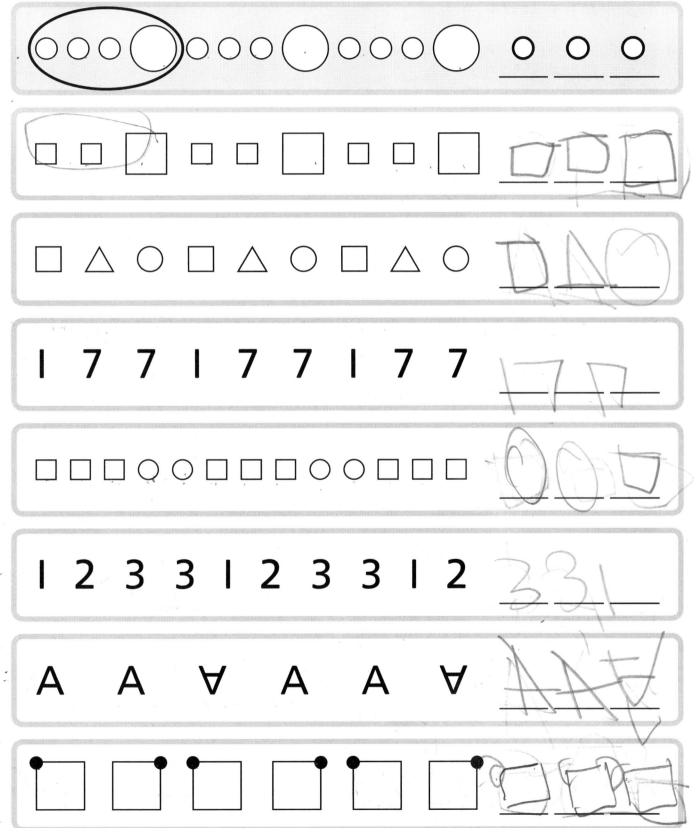

# What Changes?

Which **attribute** changes?

size      (direction)

shape      (direction)

shape      (direction)

colour      (direction)

size      (colour)      shape

direction      shape      (size)      colour

(direction)      colour      size      thickness

direction      shape      size      (thickness)

Patterns and Algebra 2-2

☐ What changes? Choose **two**.

direction     size     shape     colour     thickness

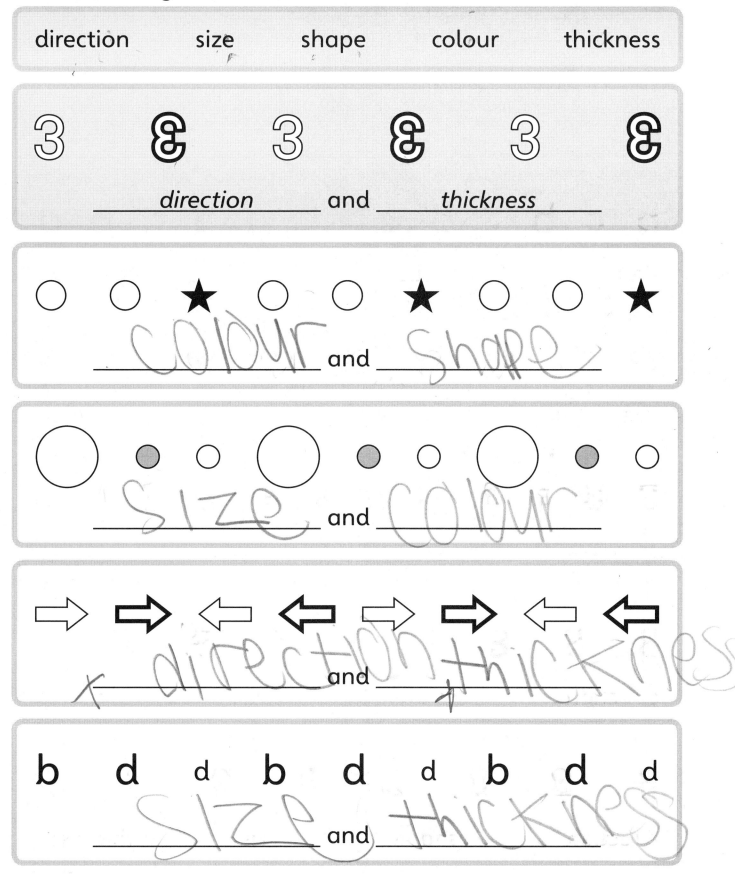

_direction_ and _thickness_

colour and shape

size and colour

direction and thickness

size and thickness

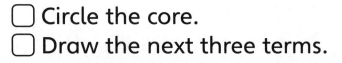

Circle the core.
Draw the next three terms.

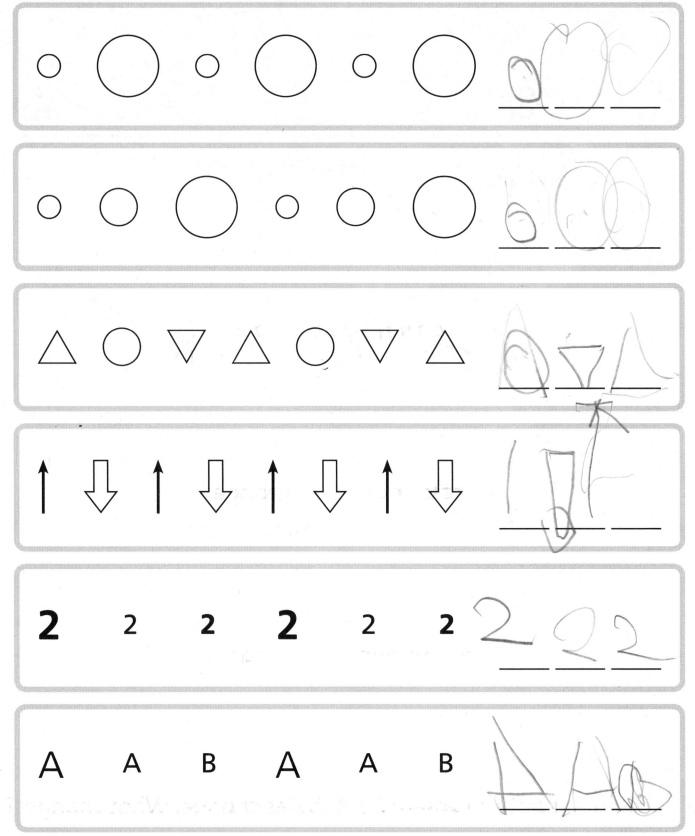

☐ Create a pattern.

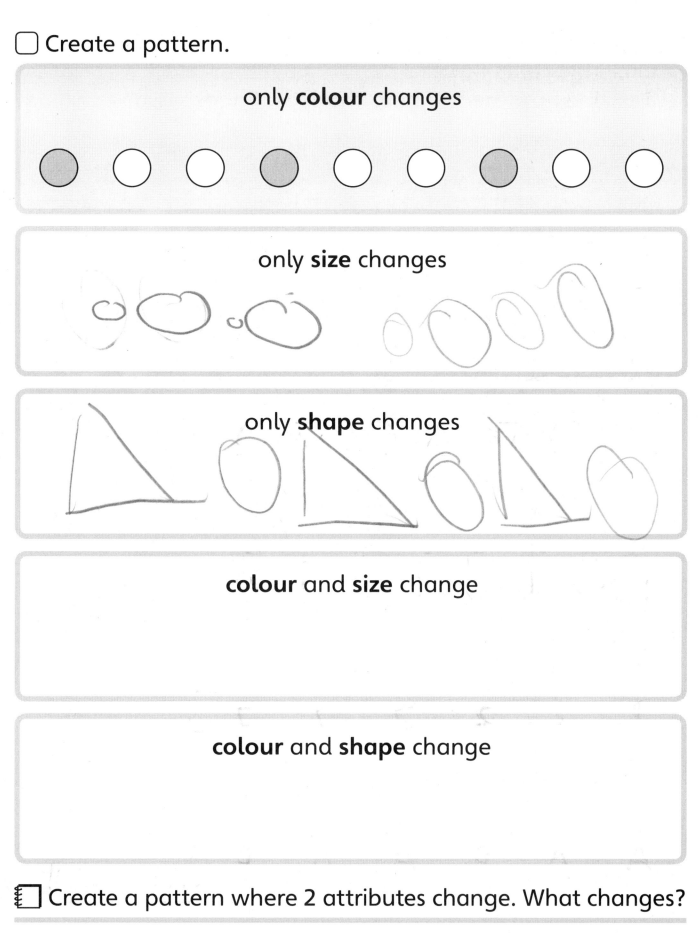

only **colour** changes

only **size** changes

only **shape** changes

**colour** and **size** change

**colour** and **shape** change

☐ Create a pattern where 2 attributes change. What changes?

# Pattern Rules

☐ Circle the core.
☐ Describe how the attribute changes. Choose two.

| thin | thick | small | big | light | dark |

(③ ③) 3 **3** 3 **3** 3 **3** 3 **3** 3 **3**

_____thin_____ , _____thick_____ , _____repeat_____

_light light_ , _dark_ , _____repeat_____

_light dark_ , _dark_ , _____repeat_____

_small_ , _small_ , _big_ , _big_ , _____repeat_____

☐ Now say when to repeat as well.

thin thin thick thin thin thin

☐ Describe how **two** attributes change.

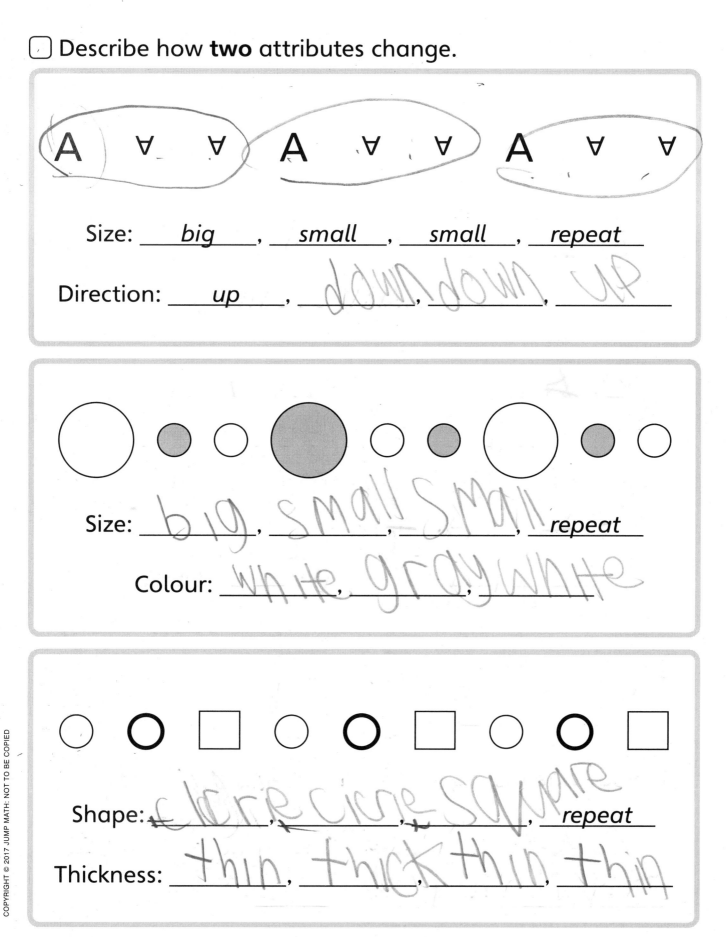

Size: _____big_____ , _____small_____ , _____small_____ , _____repeat_____

Direction: _____up_____ , _____down_____ , _____down_____ , _____up_____

Size: ___big___ , ___small___ , ___small___ , _repeat_

Colour: ___white___ , ___gray___ , ___white___

Shape: ___circle___ , ___circle___ , ___square___ , _repeat_

Thickness: ___thin___ , ___thick___ , ___thin___ , ___thin___

## ☐ Describe the pattern.

big     small     circle     triangle

_____circle_____ , _____*triangle*_____ , ___*repeat*___

_____*big*_____ , ___*small small*___ , ___*repeat*___

up     down     dark     light

_____*dark*_____ , ___*dark white white dar*___

___*dark*___ , ___*white*___ , ___*white*___

thin     thick     big     small

_____*thick*_____ , ___*thin*___ , ___*thick big*___

___*small*___ , _____ , _____ , _____

# Showing Patterns in Different Ways

☐ Use letters to show the pattern.
Put the same letter under the same figures.

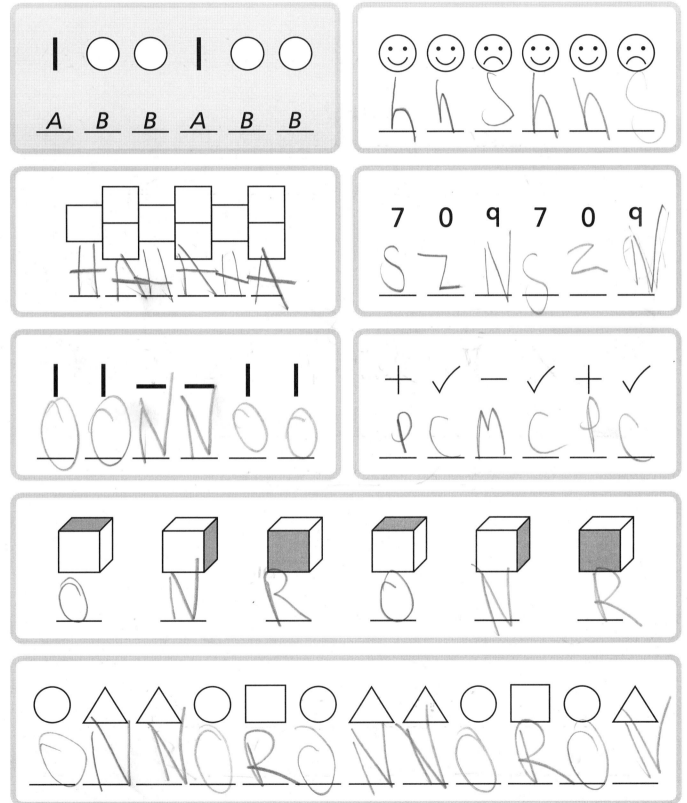

☐ Show the pattern in two ways. Use 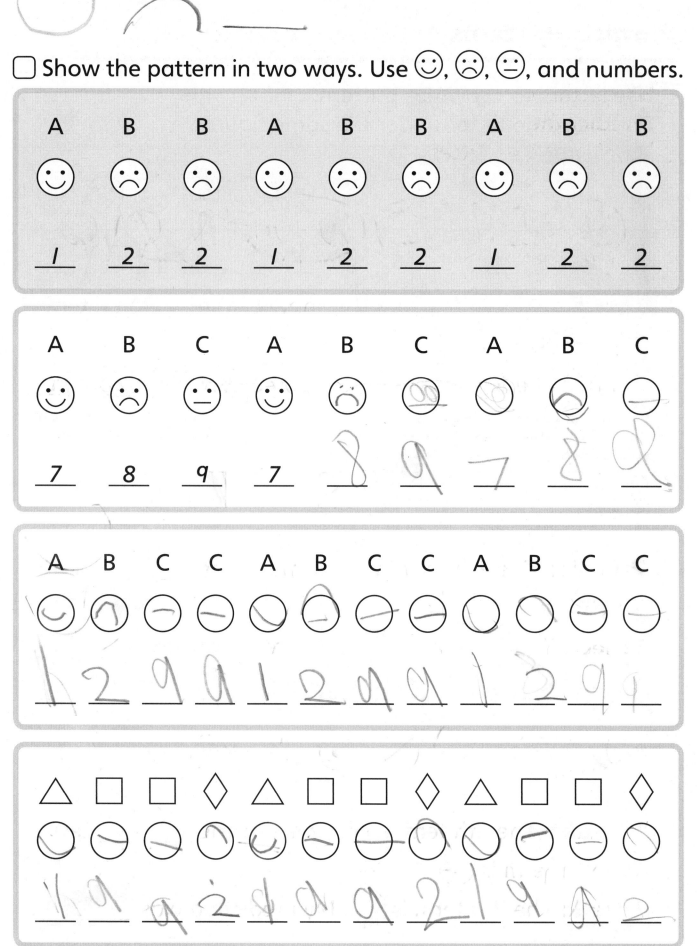, and numbers.

| A | B | B | A | B | B | A | B | B |
|---|---|---|---|---|---|---|---|---|
| 1 | 2 | 2 | 1 | 2 | 2 | 1 | 2 | 2 |

| A | B | C | A | B | C | A | B | C |
|---|---|---|---|---|---|---|---|---|
| 7 | 8 | 9 | 7 | 8 | 9 | 7 | 8 | 9 |

| A | B | C | C | A | B | C | C | A | B | C | C |
|---|---|---|---|---|---|---|---|---|---|---|---|
| 1 | 2 | 9 | 9 | 1 | 2 | 9 | 9 | 1 | 2 | 9 | 9 |

| △ | □ | □ | ◇ | △ | □ | □ | ◇ | △ | □ | □ | ◇ |
|---|---|---|---|---|---|---|---|---|---|---|---|
| 1 | 2 | 9 | 2 | 1 | 9 | 9 | 2 | 1 | 9 | 9 | 2 |

# Predicting Terms

☐ Circle the core as many times as it happens.
☐ Predict the 9th term.
☐ Continue the pattern to check.

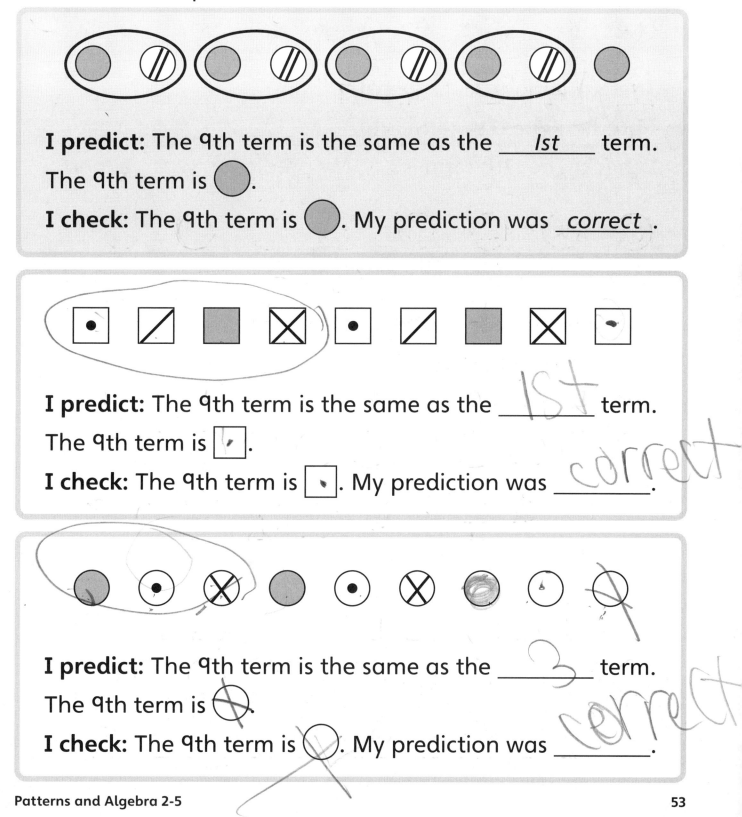

**I predict:** The 9th term is the same as the ___*lst*___ term.

The 9th term is ⬤.

**I check:** The 9th term is ⬤. My prediction was ___*correct*___.

**I predict:** The 9th term is the same as the ___lst___ term.

The 9th term is ▫.

**I check:** The 9th term is ▫. My prediction was ___correct___.

**I predict:** The 9th term is the same as the ___3___ term.

The 9th term is ⊘.

**I check:** The 9th term is ⊘. My prediction was ___correct___.

☐ Circle the core.
☐ Predict the term.
☐ Check.

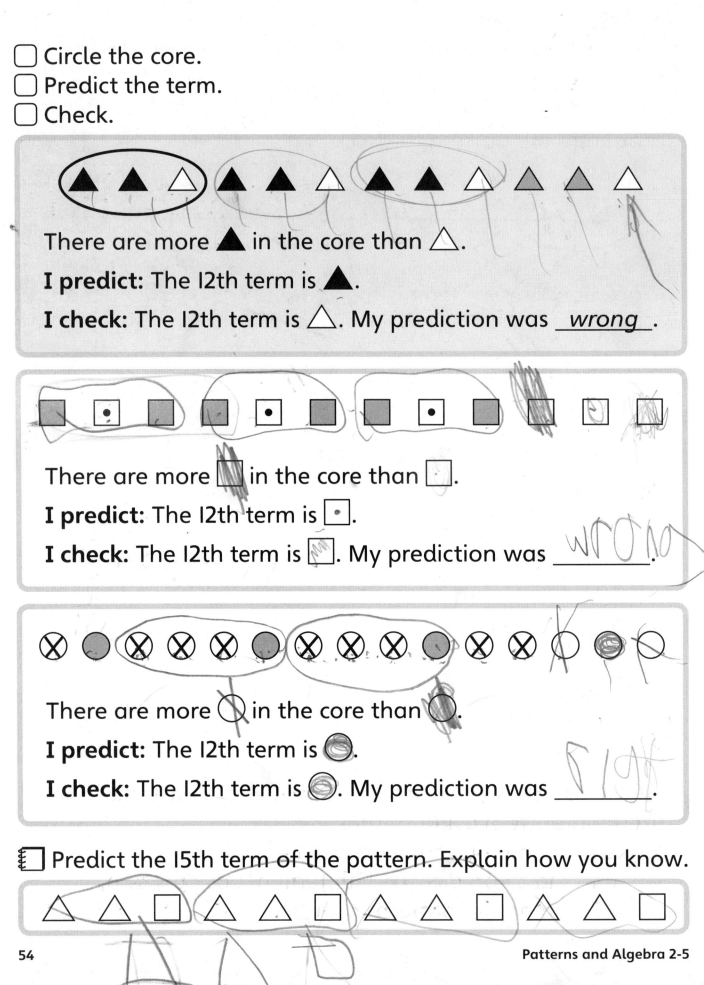

There are more ▲ in the core than △.

**I predict:** The 12th term is ▲.

**I check:** The 12th term is △. My prediction was _wrong_.

There are more ■ in the core than ⊡.

**I predict:** The 12th term is ⊡.

**I check:** The 12th term is ■. My prediction was _wrong_.

There are more ⊗ in the core than ◉.

**I predict:** The 12th term is ◉.

**I check:** The 12th term is ◉. My prediction was _____.

☐ Predict the 15th term of the pattern. Explain how you know.

# Problems and Puzzles

☐ Circle the core.

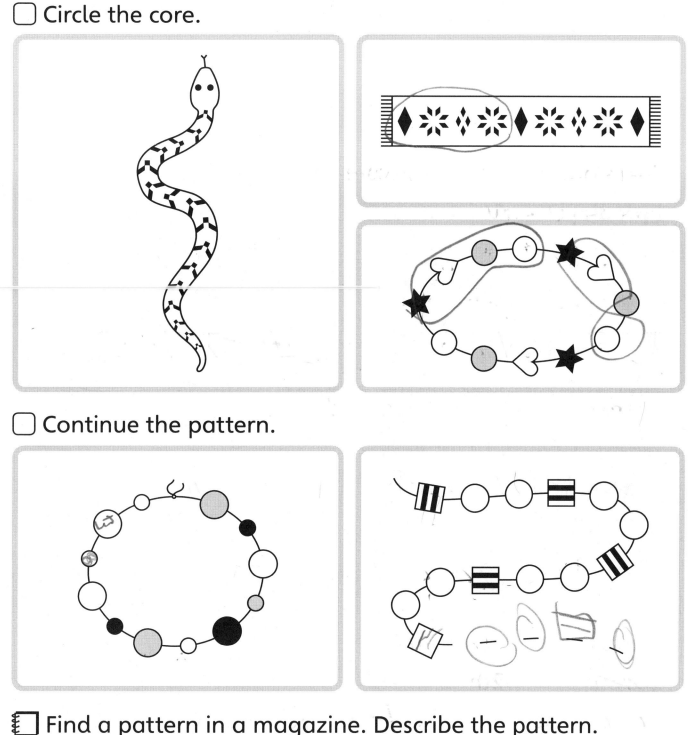

☐ Continue the pattern.

📓 Find a pattern in a magazine. Describe the pattern.
📓 Create a pattern using shapes.
   Make the same pattern with letters.
   Ask a friend to predict the 15th term of your pattern,
   then to extend the pattern to check.

☐ In each Canadian postal code, write **N** under the numbers and **L** under the letters.

M9N 7Z4

L6Y 2A4

R3X 5B8

☐ Circle the Canadian postal codes.

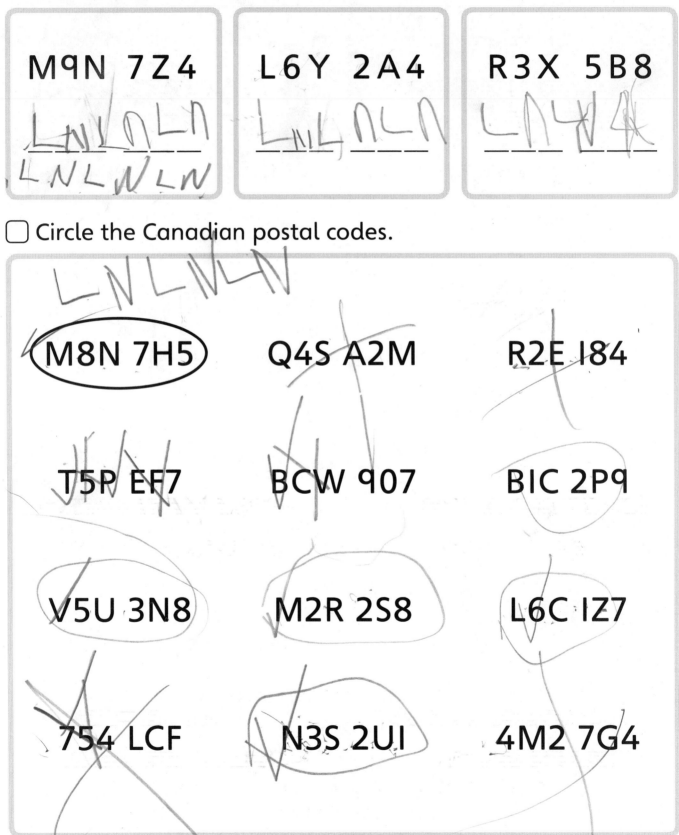

(M8N 7H5)     Q4S A2M     R2E 184

T5P EF7     BCW 907     BIC 2P9

V5U 3N8     M2R 2S8     L6C IZ7

754 LCF     N3S 2UI     4M2 7G4

**Patterns and Algebra 2-6**

# Length

☐ Colour the **longer** pencil.

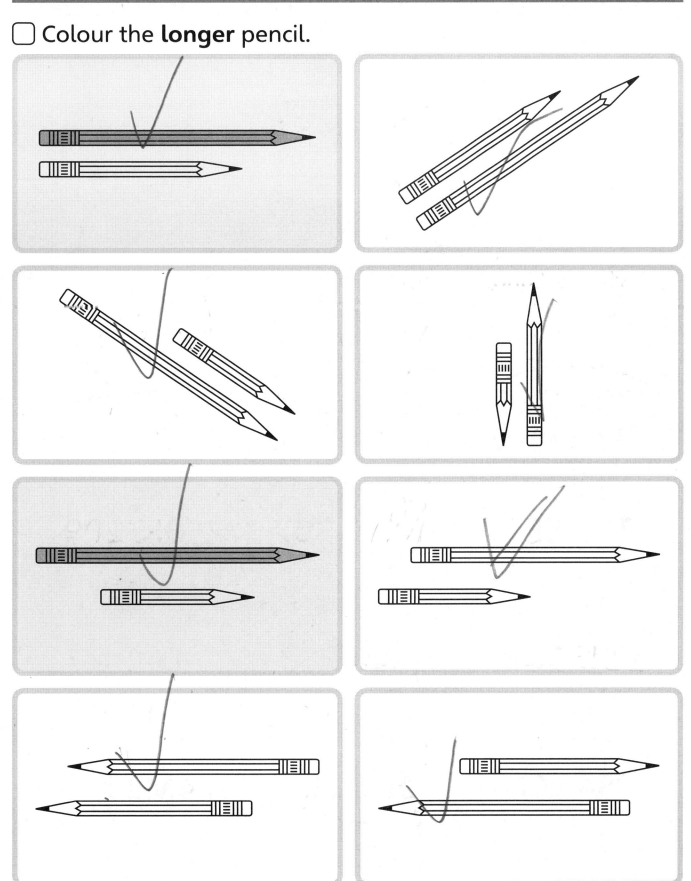

☐ Cut 4 strips of paper. Is the top **longer** or **shorter** than the side? Use the strips to compare.

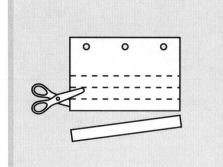 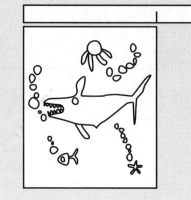 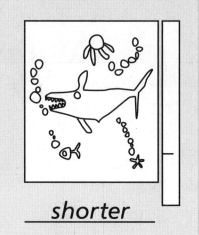

_____shorter_____

+ longer

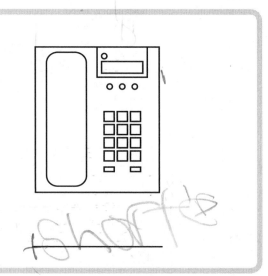

+ shorter

+ longer

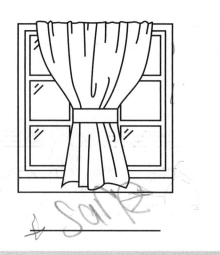

+ same

Measurement 2-1

# Width, Height, and Distance Around

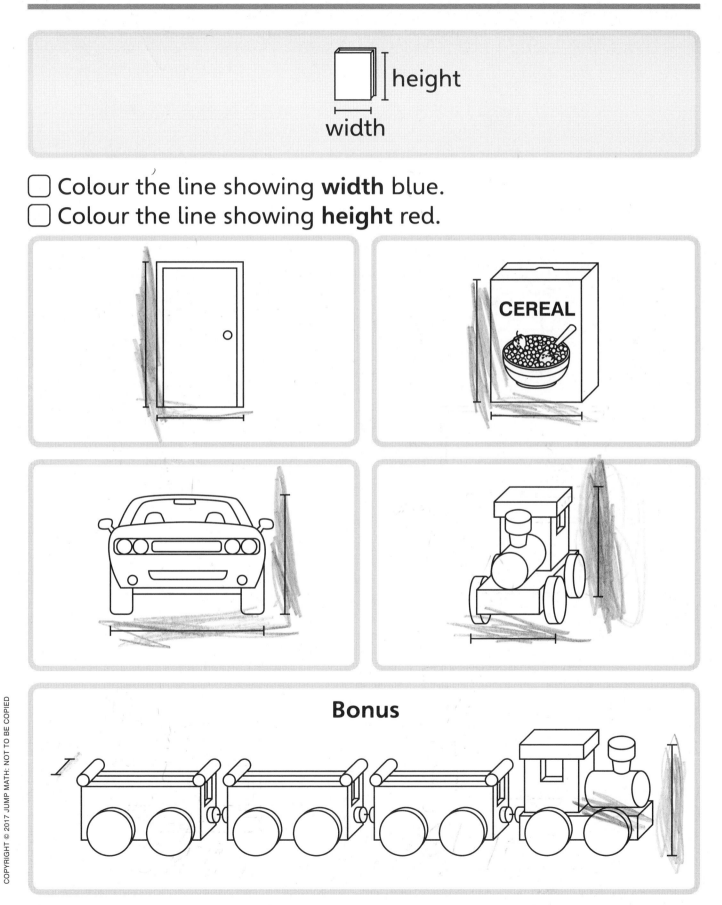

height

width

☐ Colour the line showing **width** blue.
☐ Colour the line showing **height** red.

## Bonus

☐ Write **long** or **short**.

This car is ___short___.

This car is ___long___.

This train is ___long___.

This train is ___short___.

This paper clip is ___long___.

This paper clip is ___short___.

This pencil is ___short___.

This pencil is ___long___.

☐ Which is **longer**?

The long car or the short train. ___the train___

The long paper clip or the short pencil. ___paper clip___

⬡ Name the children.

Billy says Marko is tall.
Sam says Marko is short.

Sam     Marko     Billy

Rob says Jax has short hair.
Rob says Tom has long hair.

Tom     Rob     Jax

**Bonus**
Tessa says Mary has short hair.
Rani says Sharon has short hair.
Tessa says Sharon has long hair.

Rani     Tessa     Tessa

☐ Cut a string to match the distance around.
☐ Label the string.

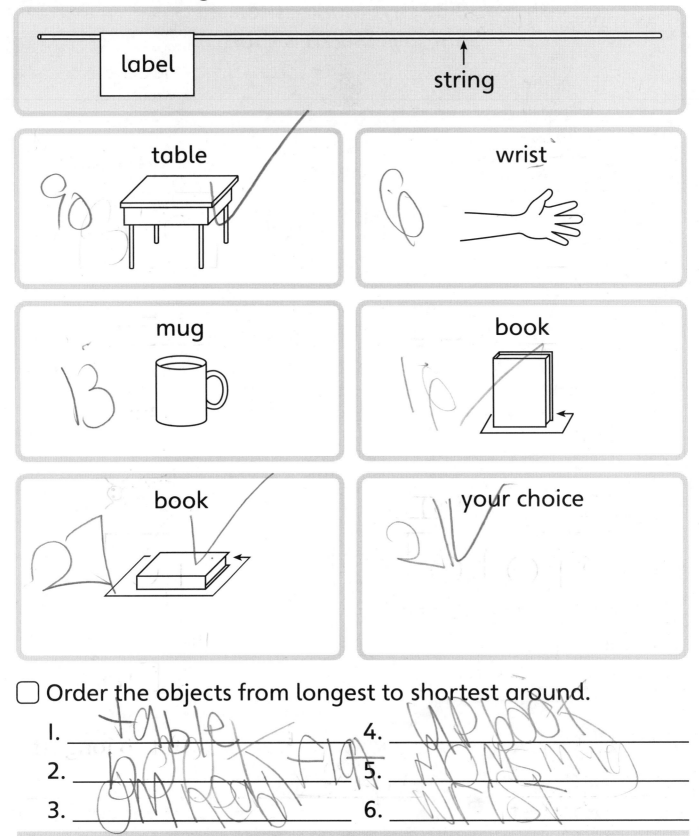

label

string

table

wrist

mug

book

book

your choice

☐ Order the objects from longest to shortest around.

1. _____  4. _____

2. _____  5. _____

3. _____  6. _____

**Measurement 2-2**

# Measuring Length

Use big 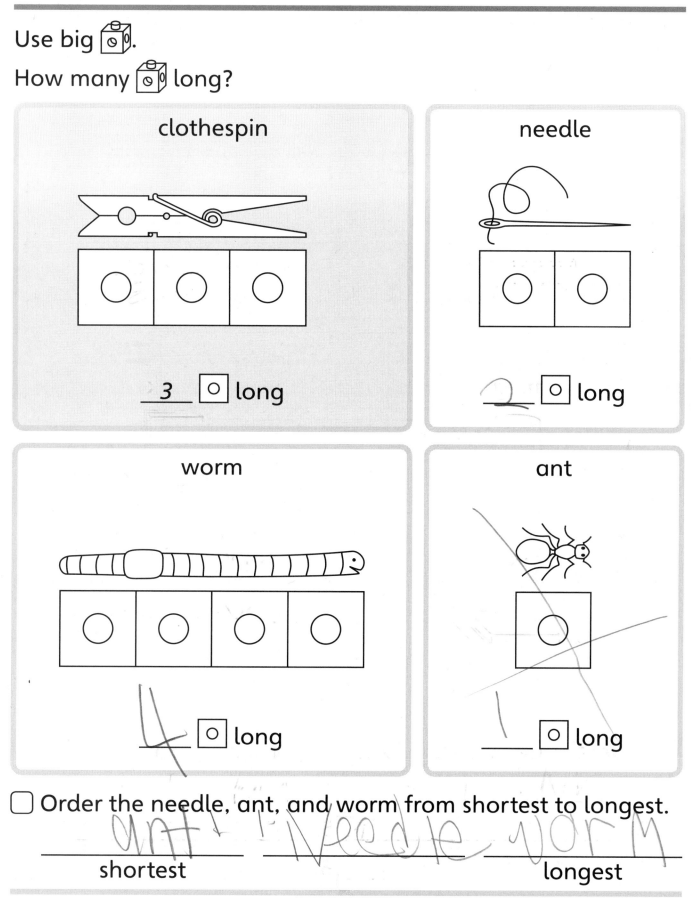.

How many long?

clothespin

__3__ long

needle

__2__ long

worm

__4__ long

ant

____ long

☐ Order the needle, ant, and worm from shortest to longest.

__ant__    __Needle__    __worm__
shortest                    longest

## ☐ What is the length closer to?

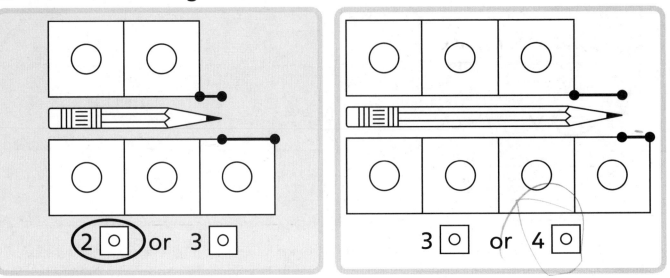

2 [○] or 3 [○]

3 [○] or 4 [○]

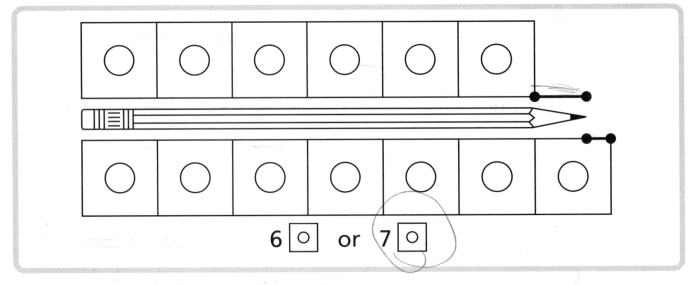

6 [○] or 7 [○]

## ☐ Measure with big [□].

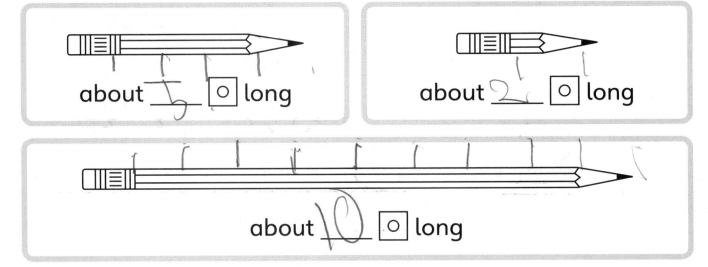

about __5__ [○] long

about __2__ [○] long

about __10__ [○] long

# Units

☐ Circle what you would use to measure the length.
☐ Explain your choice.

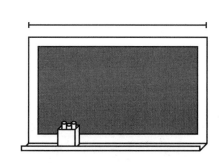

PAPERCLIPS
_____

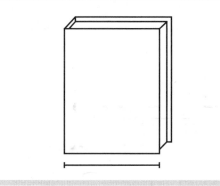
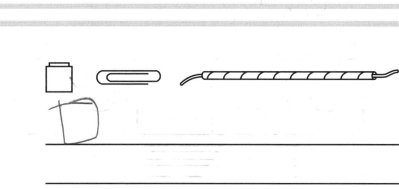

_____

PAPER CLIP.
_____

ERASER
_____

# How to Measure

Explain what is wrong with the measurement.

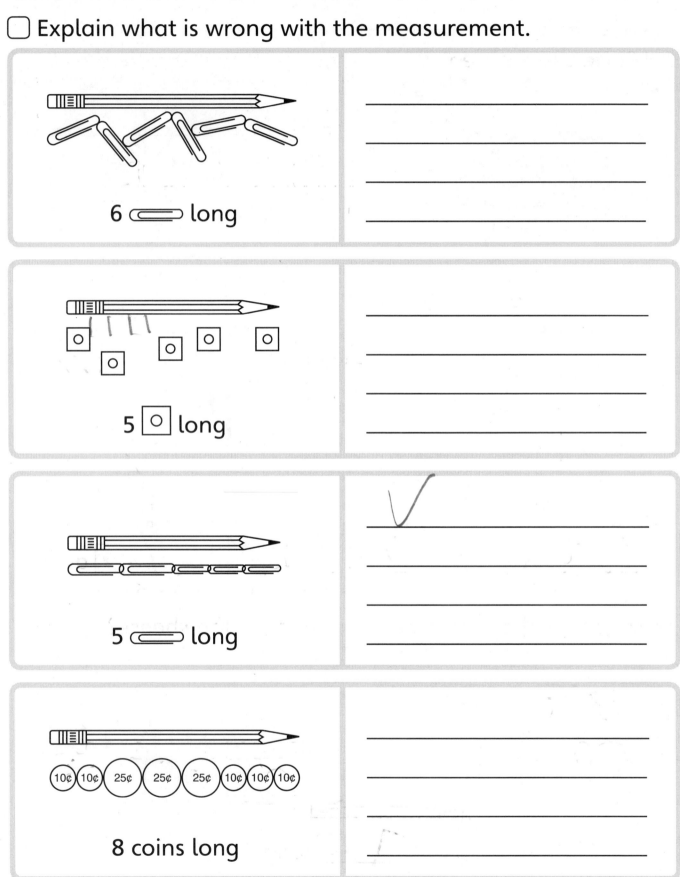

6 🖇 long

_____
_____
_____
_____

5 ▢ long

_____
_____
_____
_____

5 🖇 long

✓
_____
_____
_____
_____

8 coins long

_____
_____
_____
_____

# Measuring Distance

☐ How far is the mouse from the cheese? Use big 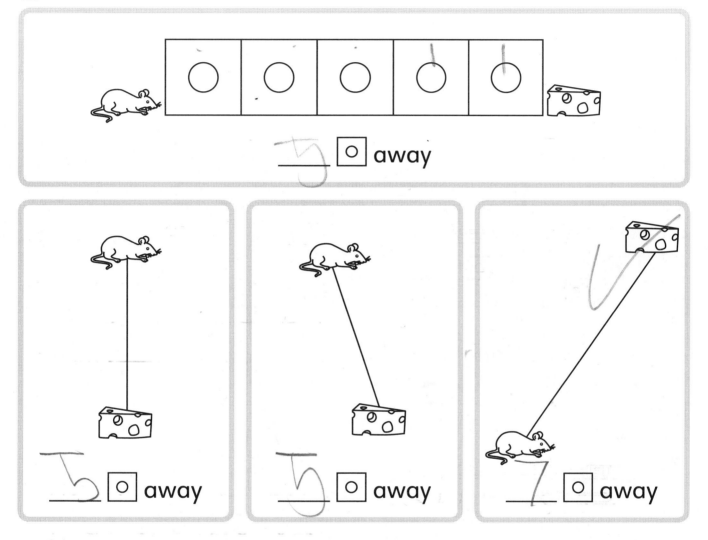.
☐ Circle the mouse that is the farthest from the cheese.

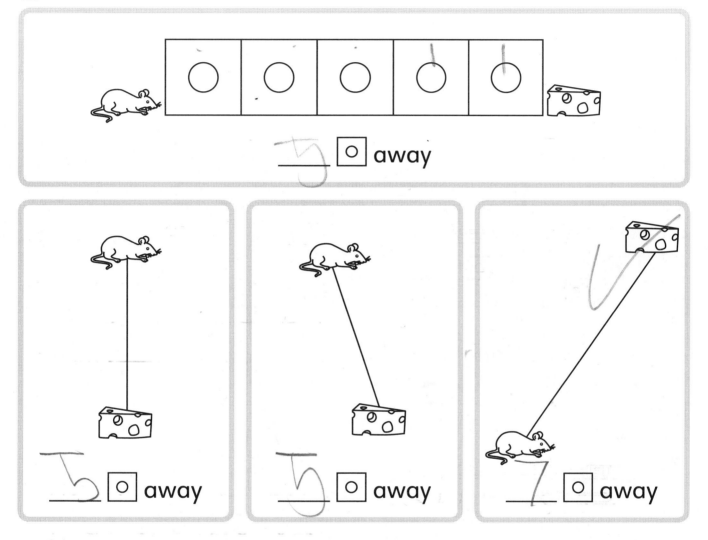

_5_ ☐ away

_5_ ☐ away    _5_ ☐ away    _7_ ☐ away

How long is the path from the mouse to the cheese?

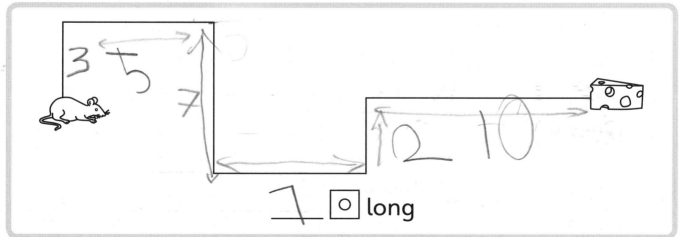

3 5 7 12 10

_7_ ☐ long

# Measuring the Distance Around

Use small 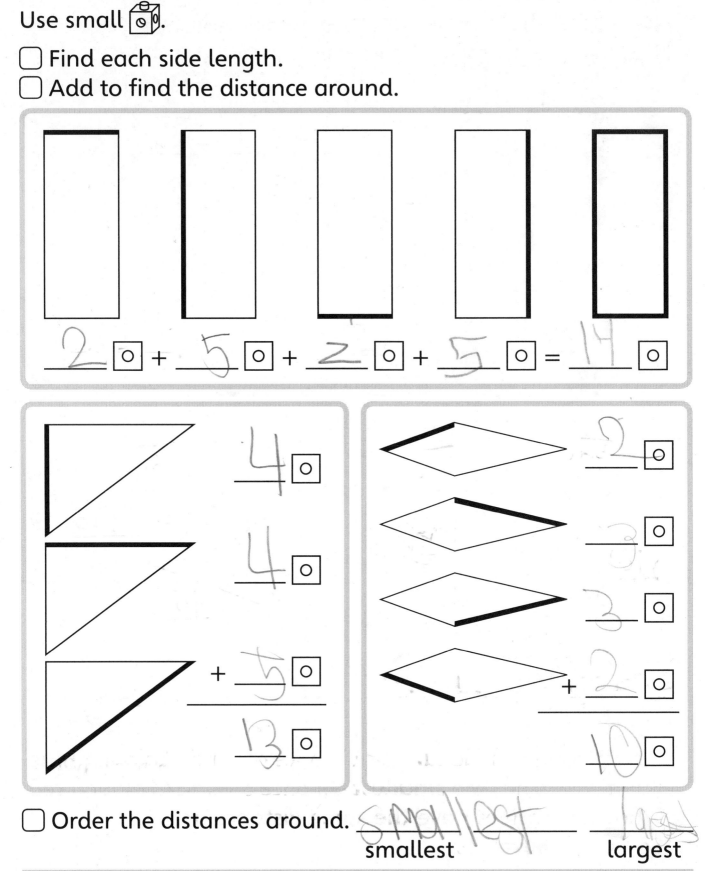.

☐ Find each side length.
☐ Add to find the distance around.

___2___ ⊡ + ___5___ ⊡ + ___2___ ⊡ + ___5___ ⊡ = ___14___ ⊡

___4___ ⊡

___4___ ⊡

+ ___5___ ⊡

___13___ ⊡

___2___ ⊡

___3___ ⊡

___3___ ⊡

+ ___2___ ⊡

___10___ ⊡

☐ Order the distances around. ___smallest___  ___largest___

smallest                    largest

**Measurement 2-7**

☐ Use big 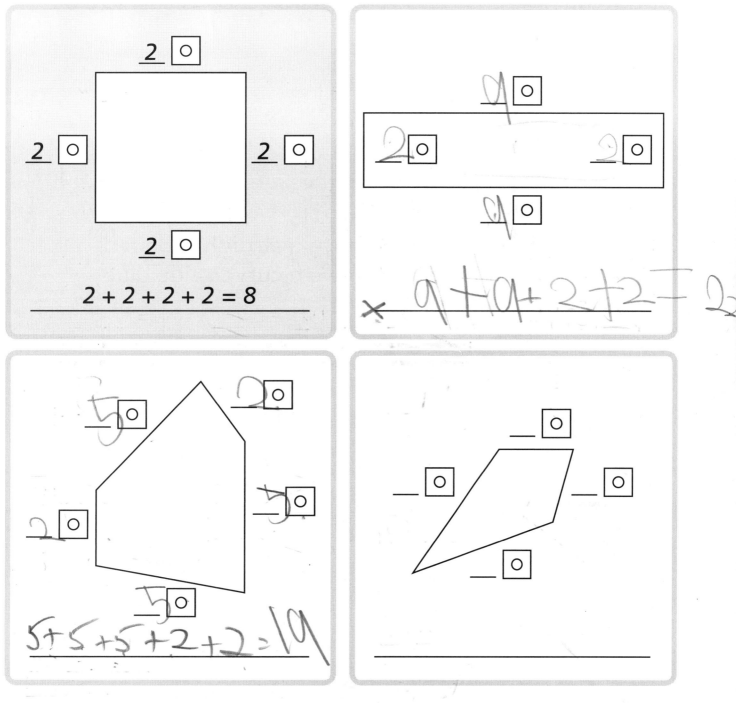 to find each side length.
☐ Write an addition sentence to show the distance around.

2 ⊙

2 ⊙        2 ⊙

2 ⊙

2 + 2 + 2 + 2 = 8

9 ⊙

2 ⊙                    2 ⊙

9 ⊙

✗ 9 + 9 + 2 + 2 = 2

5 ⊙        2 ⊙

2 ⊙        5 ⊙

5 ⊙

5 + 5 + 5 + 2 + 2 = 19

__ ⊙

__ ⊙        __ ⊙

__ ⊙

☐ What shape has the **largest** distance around? Colour it blue.
☐ What shape has the **smallest** distance around? Colour it red.
☐ What two shapes have **the same** distance around?
   Colour them yellow.

# Lines

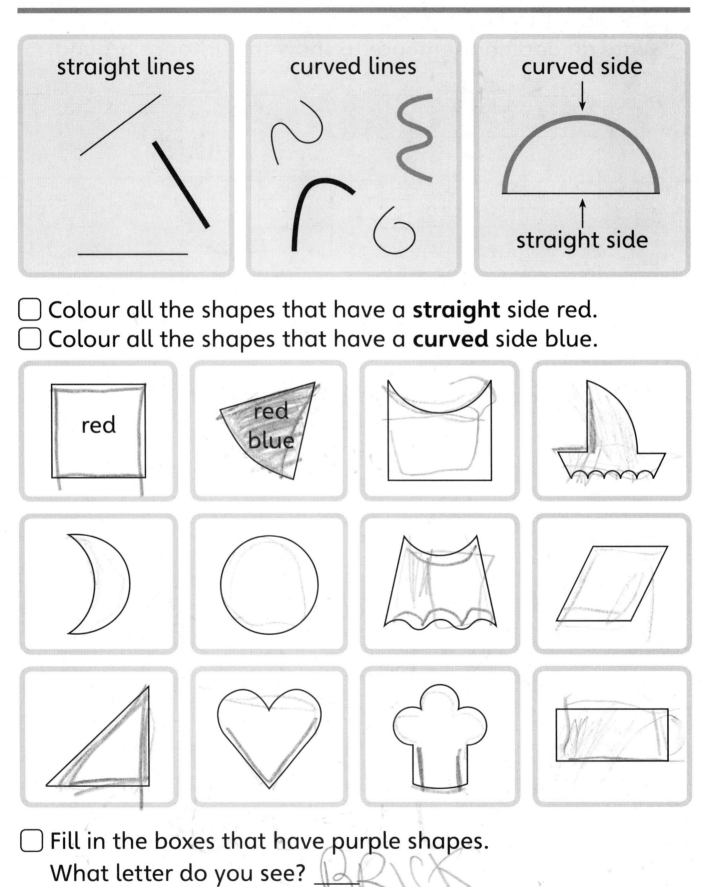

straight lines

curved lines

curved side

straight side

☐ Colour all the shapes that have a **straight** side red.
☐ Colour all the shapes that have a **curved** side blue.

red

red
blue

☐ Fill in the boxes that have purple shapes.
What letter do you see? _BRICK_

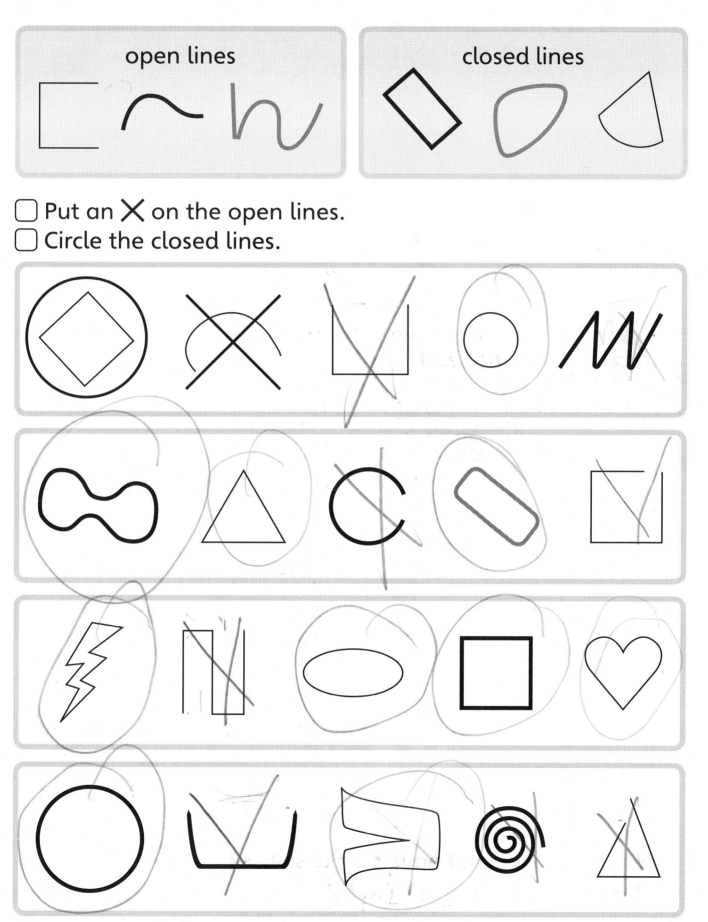

open lines

closed lines

☐ Put an ✗ on the open lines.
☐ Circle the closed lines.

# Sides and Vertices

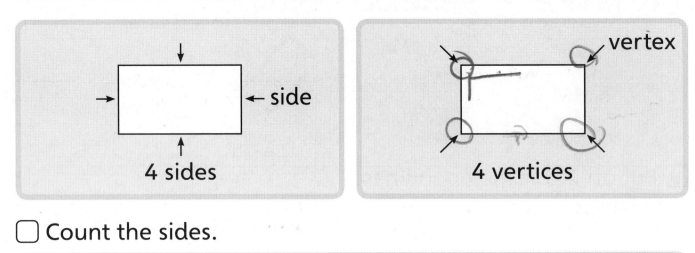

4 sides       4 vertices

☐ Count the sides.

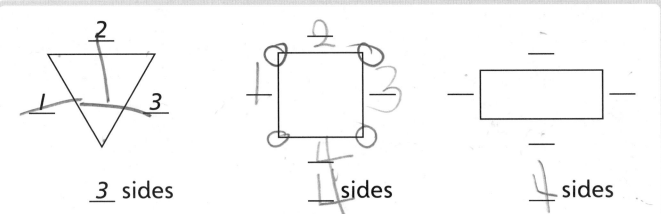

_3_ sides     _4_ sides     _4_ sides

☐ Count the vertices.

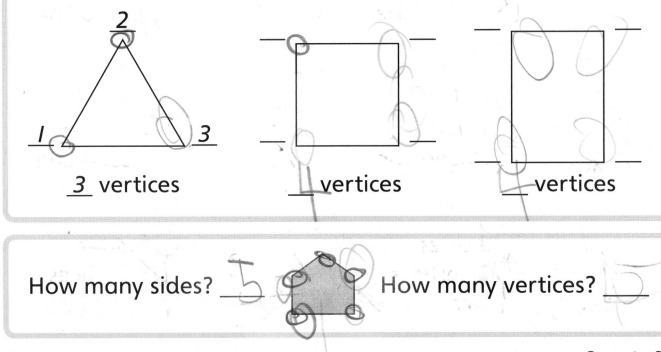

_3_ vertices     _4_ vertices     _4_ vertices

How many sides? _5_     How many vertices? _5_

Geometry 2-2

☐ ✓ what is true and ✗ what is not true.

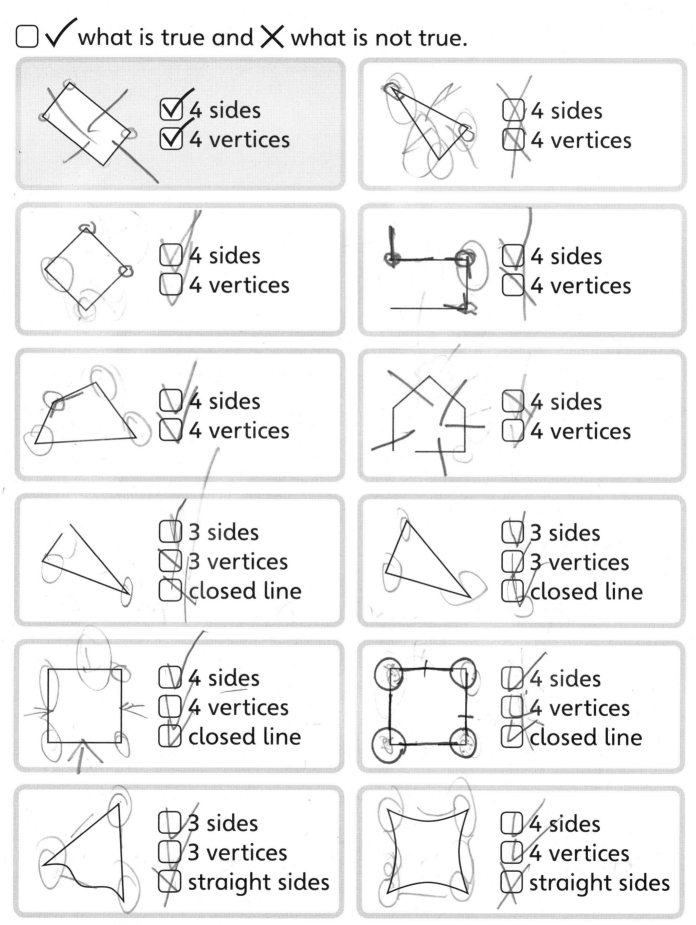

☑ 4 sides
☑ 4 vertices

☒ 4 sides
☒ 4 vertices

☑ 4 sides
☑ 4 vertices

☐ 4 sides
☐ 4 vertices

☐ 4 sides
☐ 4 vertices

☐ 4 sides
☐ 4 vertices

☐ 3 sides
☒ 3 vertices
☐ closed line

☐ 3 sides
☐ 3 vertices
☐ closed line

☐ 4 sides
☐ 4 vertices
☐ closed line

☐ 4 sides
☐ 4 vertices
☐ closed line

☐ 3 sides
☐ 3 vertices
☒ straight sides

☐ 4 sides
☐ 4 vertices
☒ straight sides

# Squares

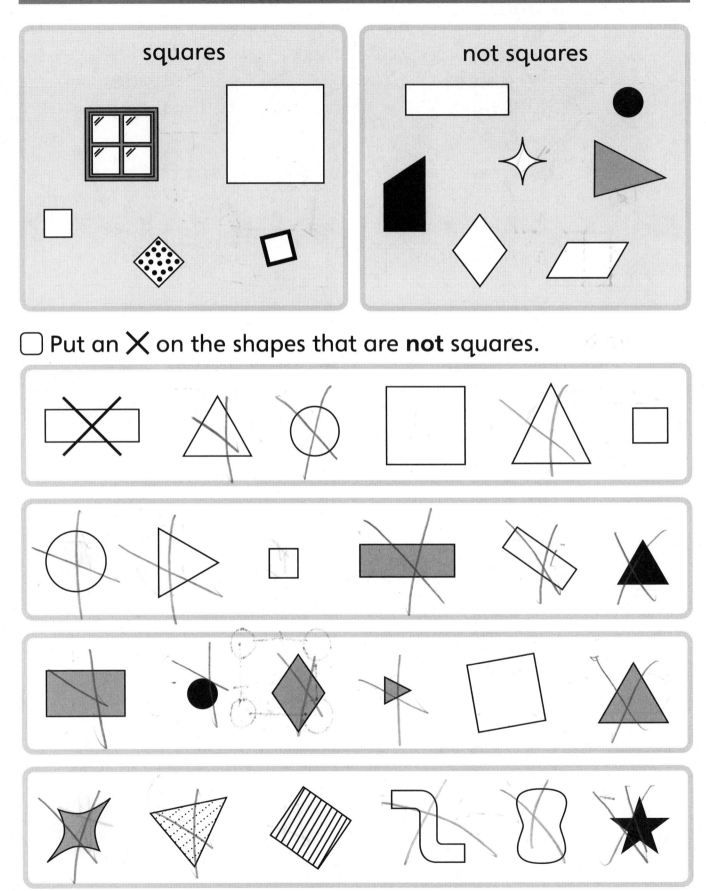

squares

not squares

☐ Put an ✗ on the shapes that are **not** squares.

# Rectangles

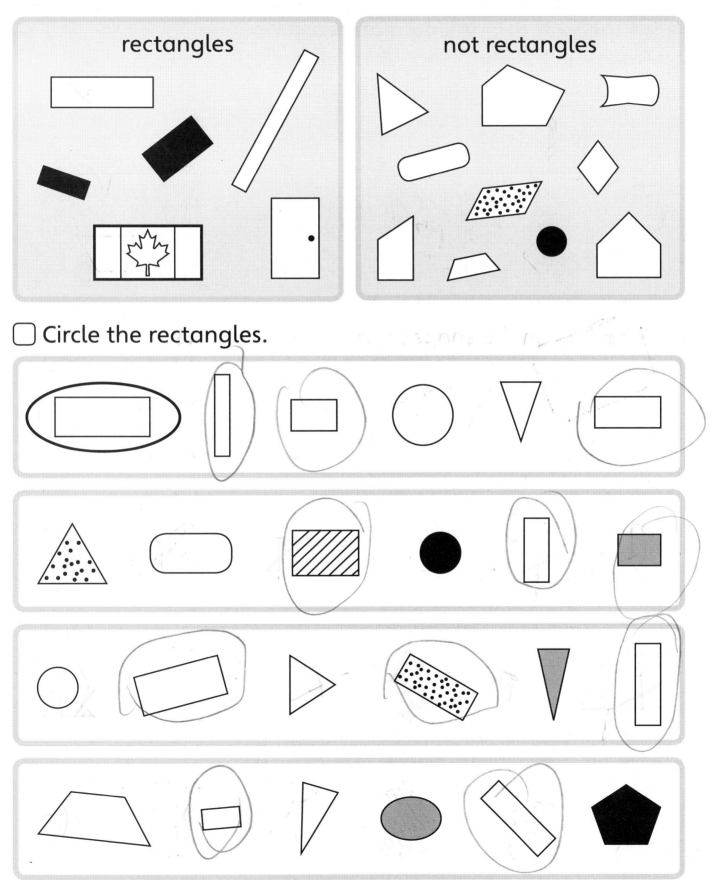

rectangles

not rectangles

☐ Circle the rectangles.

☐ Place a pattern block square on the
   shape so that one side matches.
☐ Trace the pattern block. Does it match?
☐ ✓ what is true and ✗ what is not true.

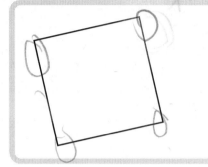 ☑ 4 sides        ☑ square
☑ 4 corners
☑ all sides equal

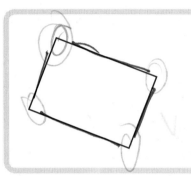 ☑ 4 sides        ☒ square
☑ 4 corners     ☑ rectangle
☒ all sides equal

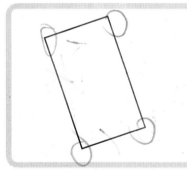 ☑ 4 sides        ☒ square
☑ 4 corners     ☑ rectangle
☒ all sides equal

☐ Draw.

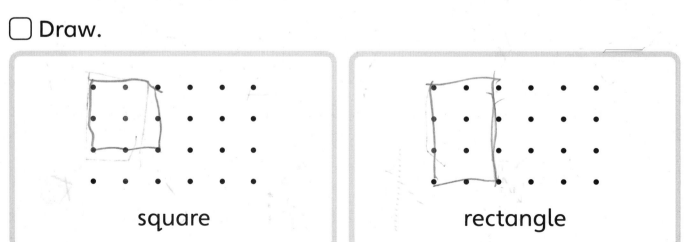

square                    rectangle

Geometry 2-4

# Triangles

triangles

not triangles

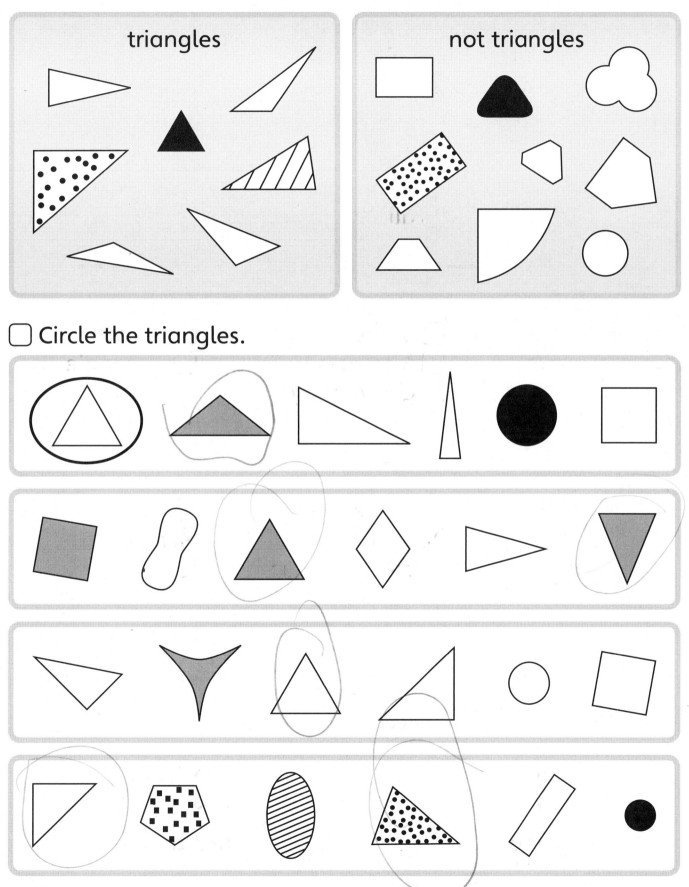

⬚ Circle the triangles.

# Circles

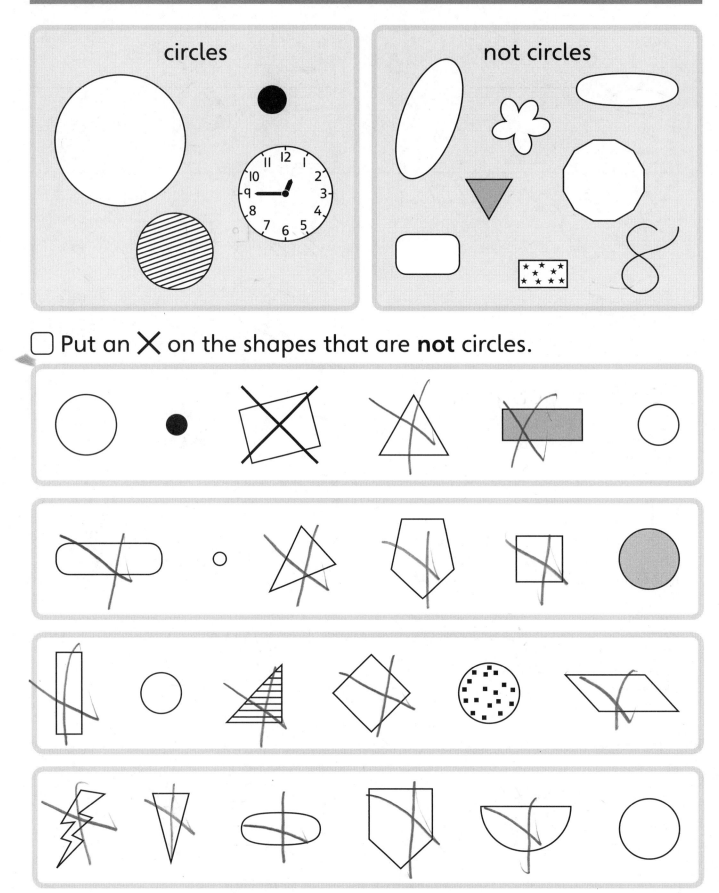

| circles | not circles |

□ Put an ✕ on the shapes that are **not** circles.

# Polygons

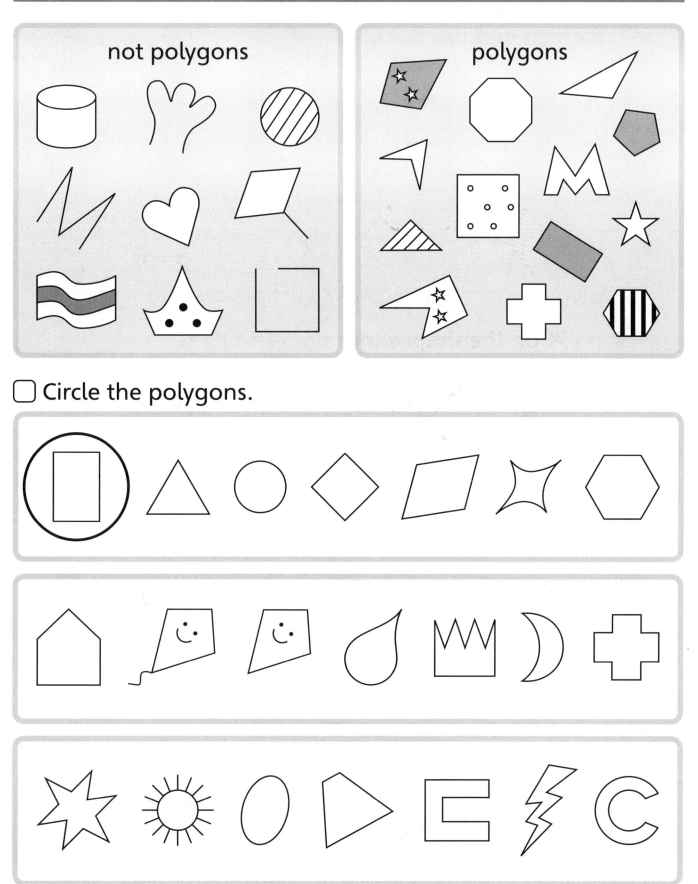

not polygons

polygons

☐ Circle the polygons.

☐ Use a ruler. Connect the dots in order.
☐ Join the first and last dots.

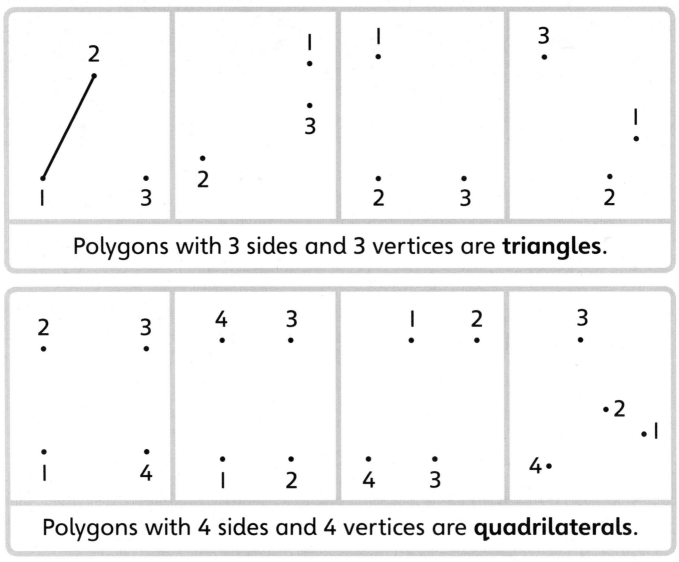

Polygons with 3 sides and 3 vertices are **triangles**.

Polygons with 4 sides and 4 vertices are **quadrilaterals**.

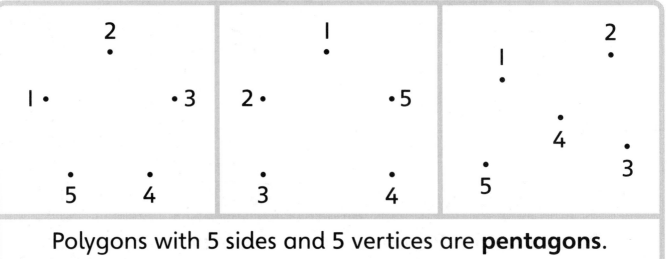

Polygons with 5 sides and 5 vertices are **pentagons**.

☐ Use a ruler. Connect the dots in order.
☐ Join the first and last dots.

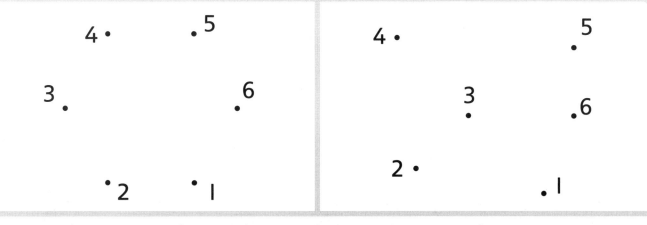

Polygons with 6 sides and 6 vertices are **hexagons**.

Polygons with 7 sides and 7 vertices are **heptagons**.

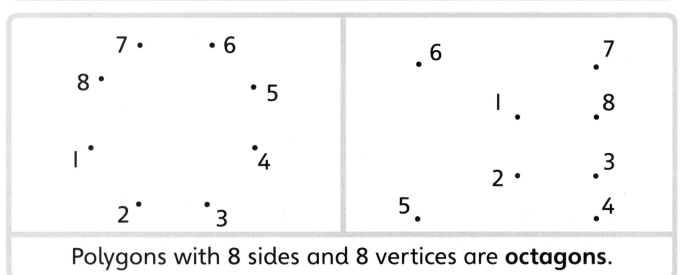

Polygons with 8 sides and 8 vertices are **octagons**.

# About Polygons

☐ Draw the missing sides to complete the shapes.
☐ Count the vertices to check.

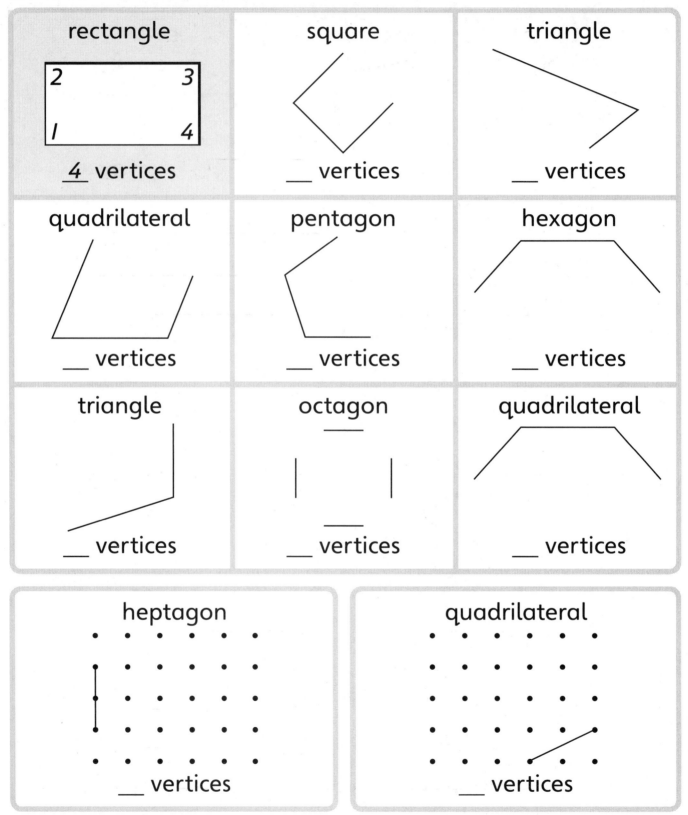

| rectangle | square | triangle |
|---|---|---|
| <u>4</u> vertices | __ vertices | __ vertices |
| quadrilateral | pentagon | hexagon |
| __ vertices | __ vertices | __ vertices |
| triangle | octagon | quadrilateral |
| __ vertices | __ vertices | __ vertices |

heptagon

__ vertices

quadrilateral

__ vertices

**Geometry 2-8**

How many sides?
How many vertices?
☐ Name the shape.

| triangle | heptagon | square |
|---|---|---|
| rectangle | quadrilateral | hexagon |
| pentagon | circle | octagon |

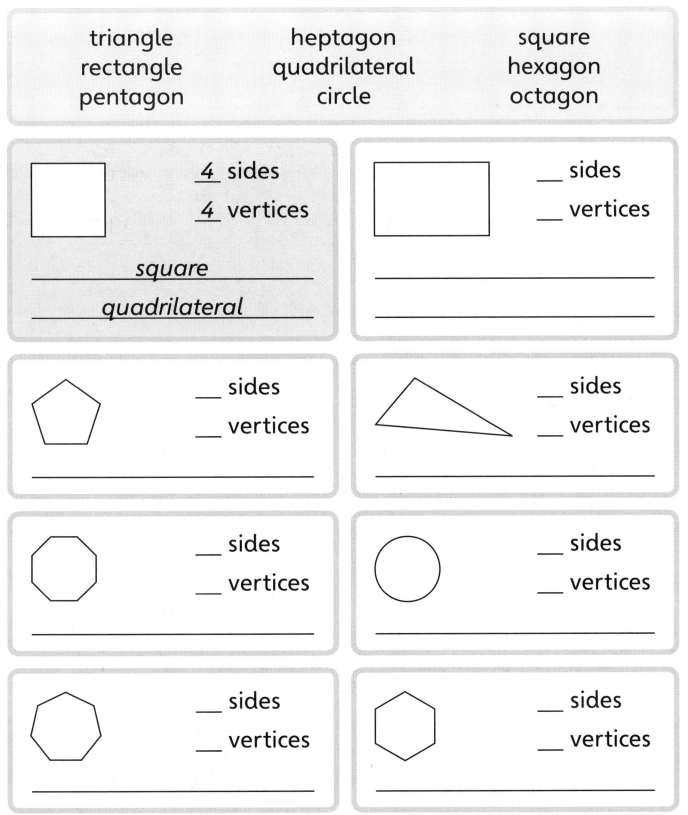

__4__ sides

__4__ vertices

_____square_____

_____quadrilateral_____

__ sides

__ vertices

_____

_____

__ sides

__ vertices

_____

__ sides

__ vertices

_____

__ sides

__ vertices

_____

__ sides

__ vertices

_____

__ sides

__ vertices

_____

__ sides

__ vertices

_____

☐ Draw an object with the same shape.

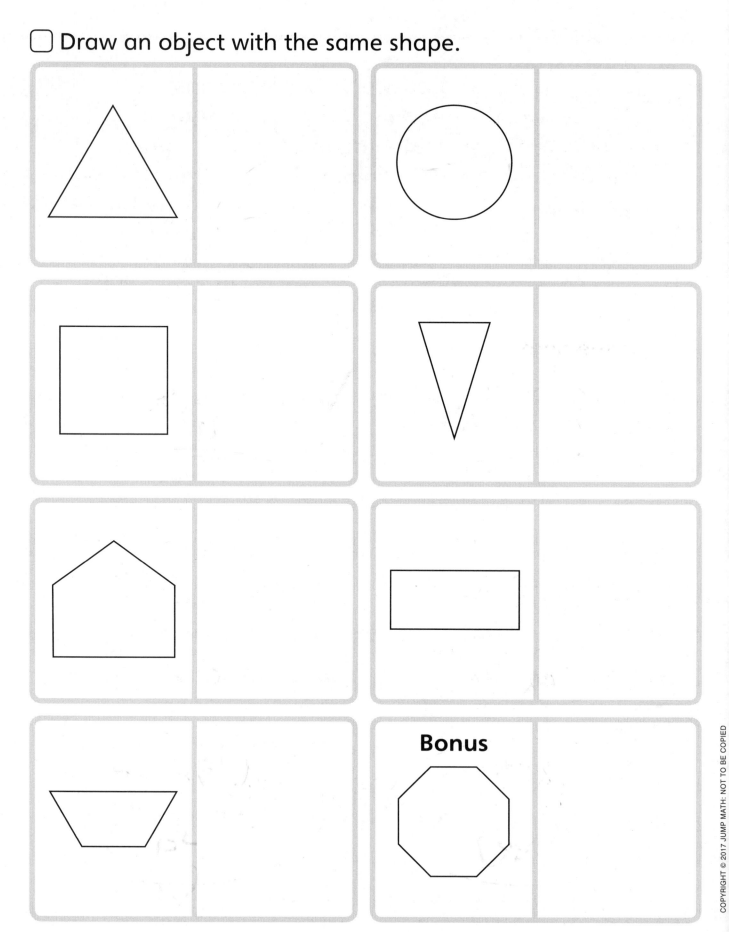

# Sorting into Groups

You can sort anything into **groups**.
The things you sort are called **data**.

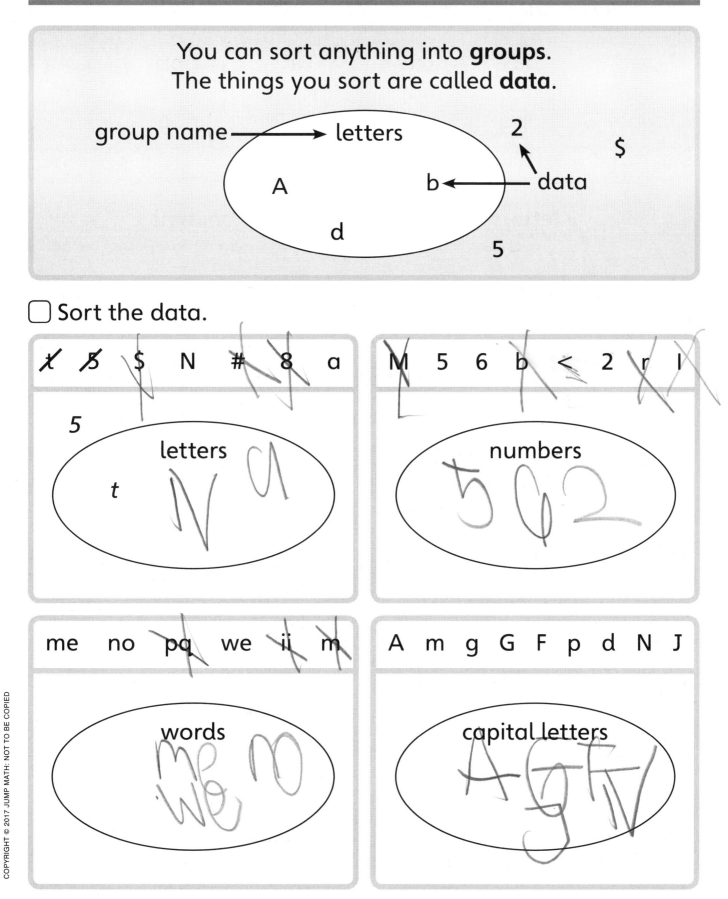

group name ⟶ letters        2

A                    b ⟵ data        $

d

5

☐ Sort the data.

X̶  B̶  $  N  #  8  a

5

letters

t

M  5  6  b  <  2  r  l

numbers

me  no  pq  we  ii  m

words

A  m  g  G  F  p  d  N  J

capital letters

☐ Sort the data.

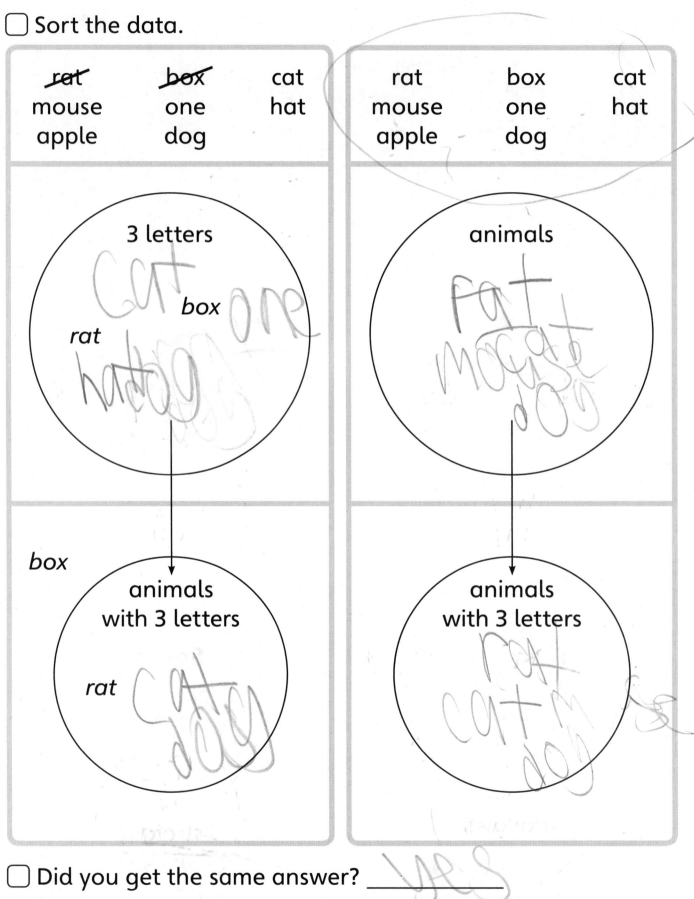

rat    box    cat
mouse  one  hat
apple  dog

rat    box    cat
mouse  one  hat
apple  dog

3 letters

rat   box

animals

box

animals
with 3 letters

rat

animals
with 3 letters

☐ Did you get the same answer? _____ yes

    **Probability and Data Management 2-1**

☐ Sort the data. Use arrows.

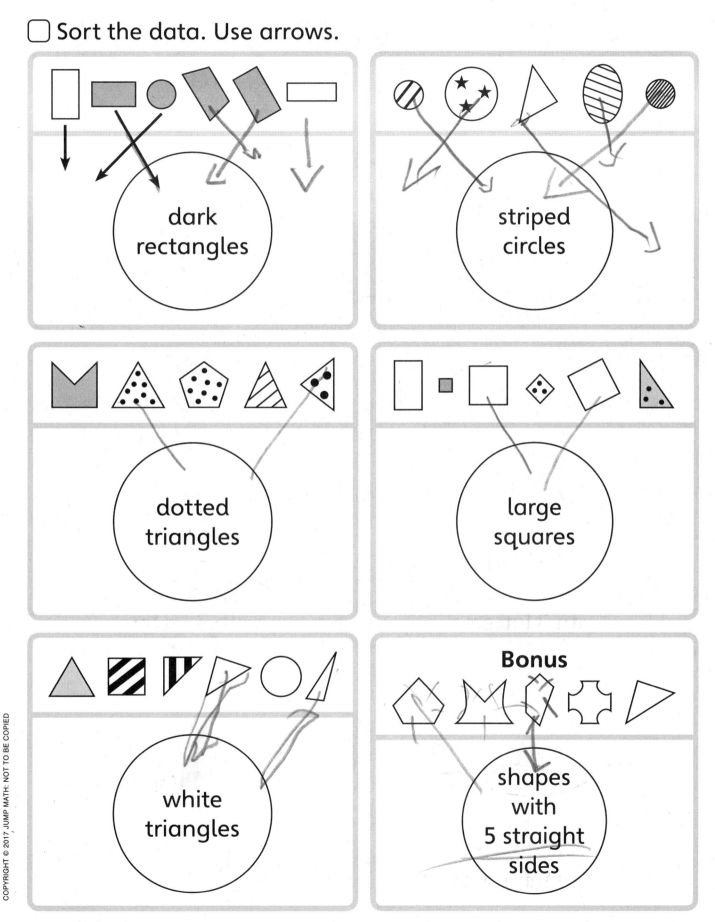

# Sorting into Many Groups

☐ Sort the data. Use arrows.

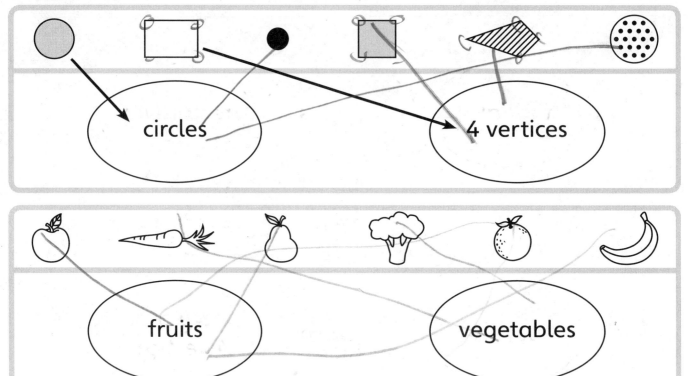

Some objects do not belong in any group.

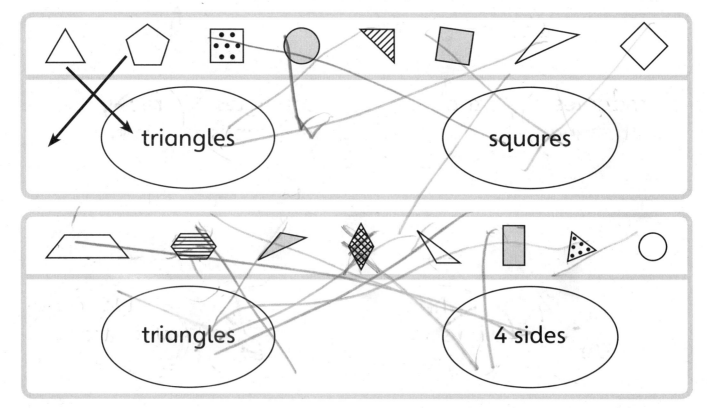

**Probability and Data Management 2-2**

☐ Sort the data. Use arrows.

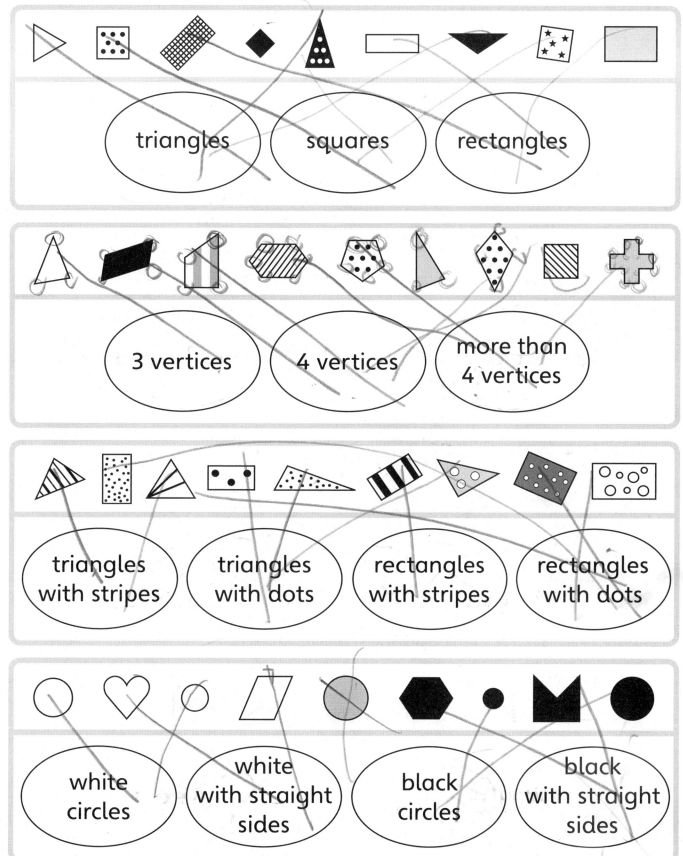

# Sorting Rules

◻ Find one word that describes the data.

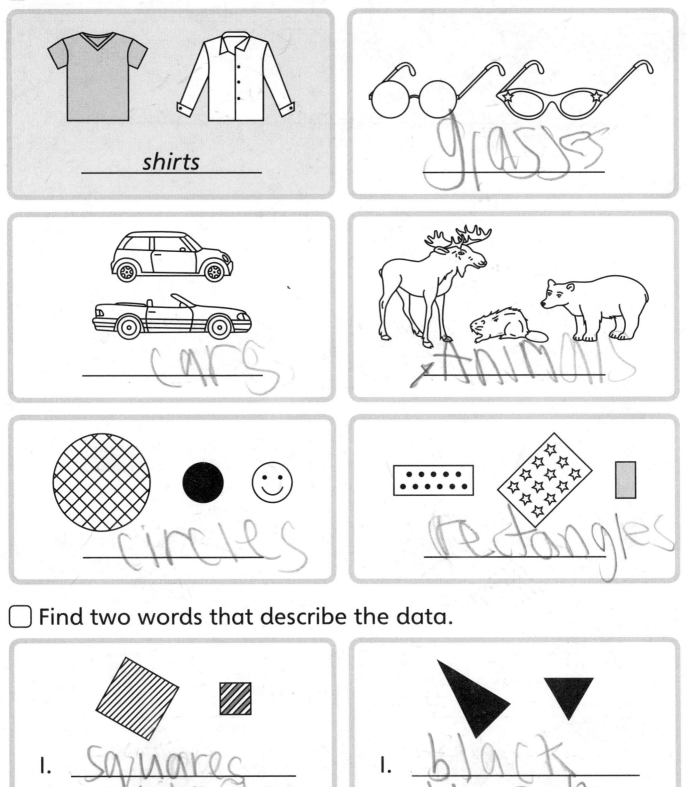

shirts

grasss

cars

Animals

circles

rectangles

◻ Find two words that describe the data.

1. squares
2. stripped

1. black
2. triangle

Probability and Data Management 2-3

How were these sorted? Write two properties.

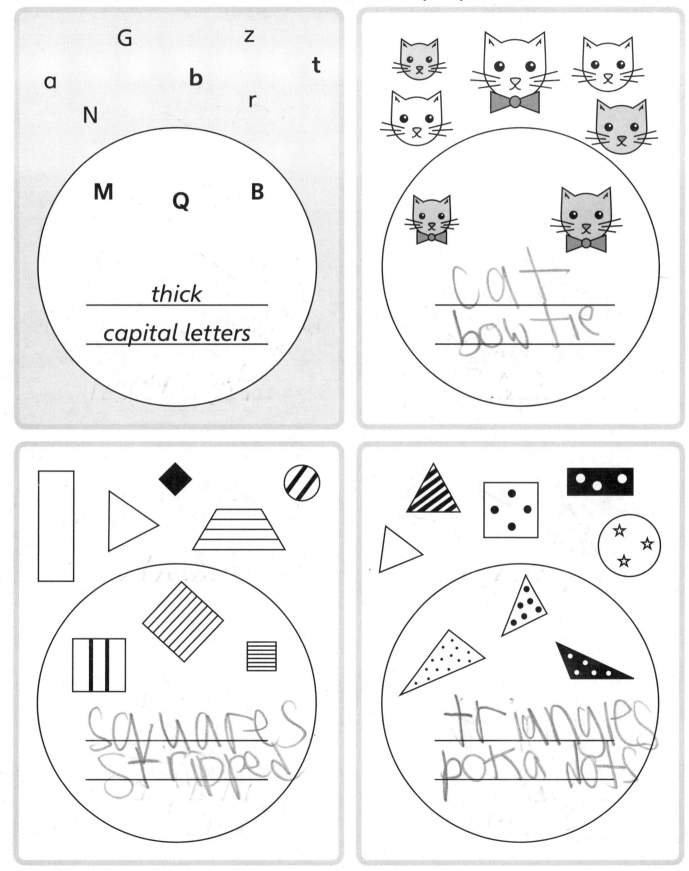

G  z
a  b  t
N  r

M  Q  B

*thick*

*capital letters*

cat

bow tie

squares

stripped

triangles

polka dots

# Sorting Rules—Many Groups

☐ How were these sorted?

new pencils
long

used pencils
short

yellow
fruits

vegetables

stripped
water

animals
mammals

**Bonus**

hop        pop
     top

op
3 letter

November

September

Months
fall

**Probability and Data Management 2-4**

☐ How were these sorted?

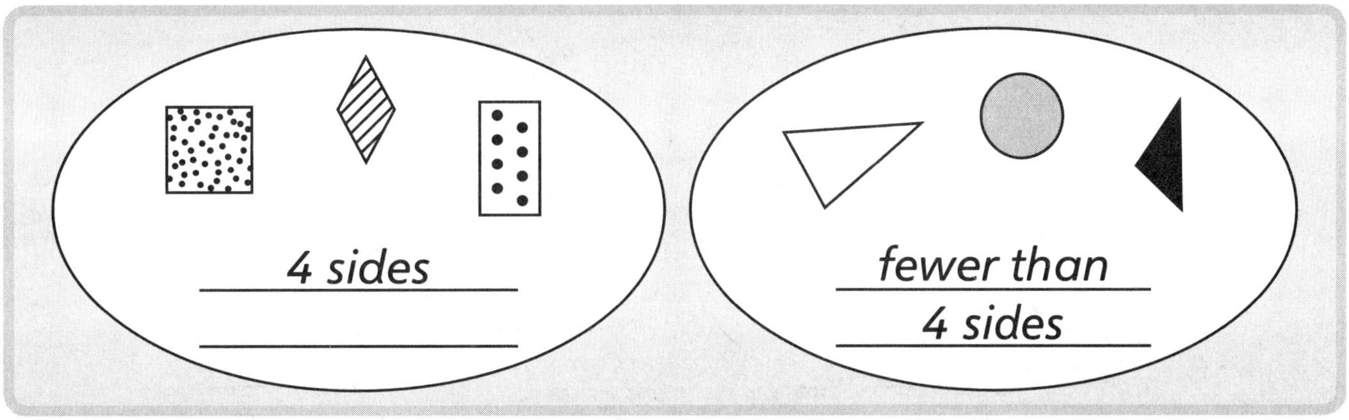

4 sides

fewer than
4 sides

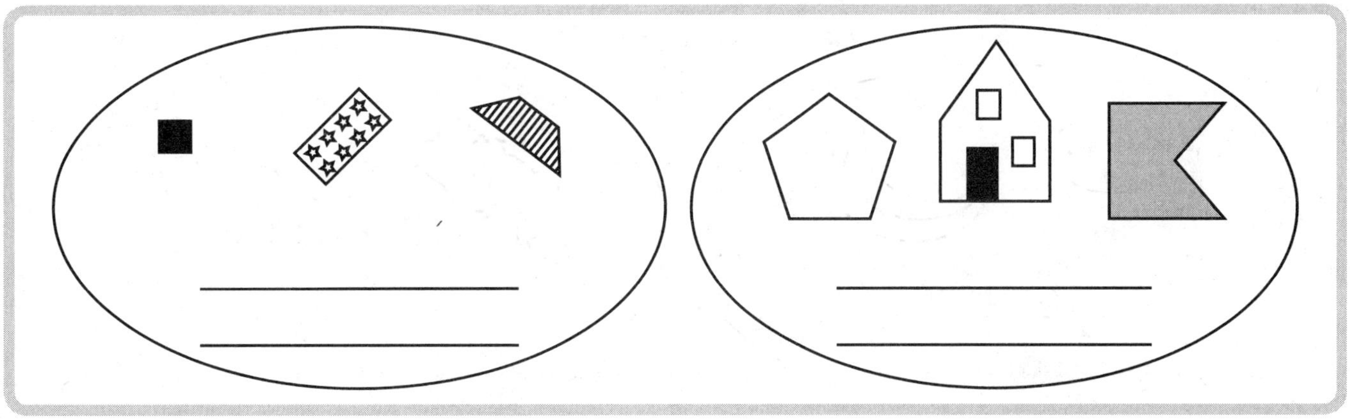

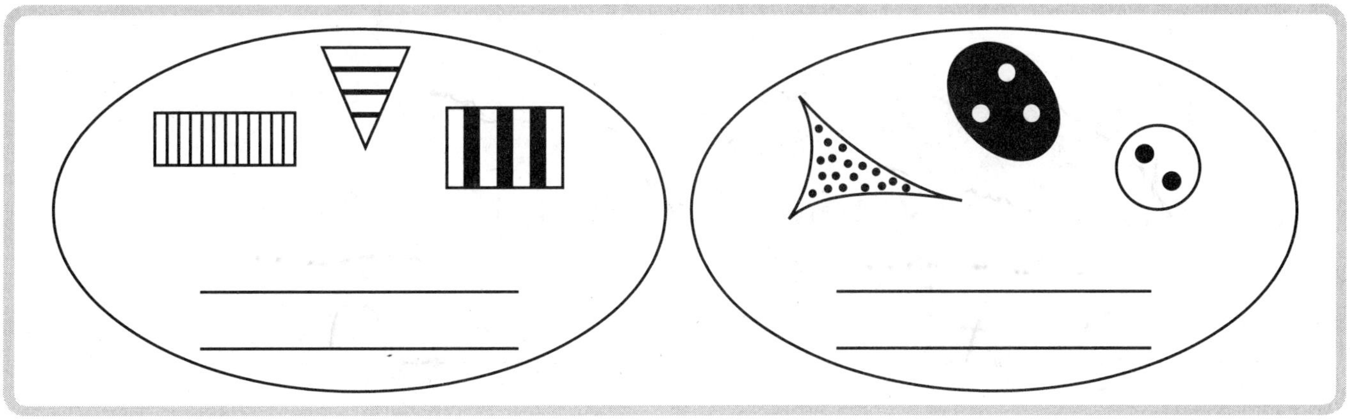

_____

_____

_____

_____

_____

_____

**Bonus**

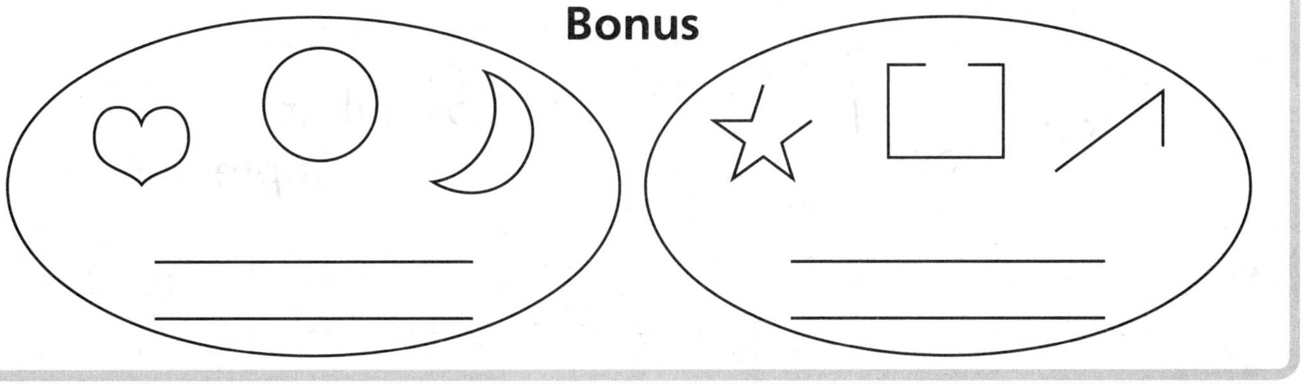

_____

_____

☐ Compare the groups.

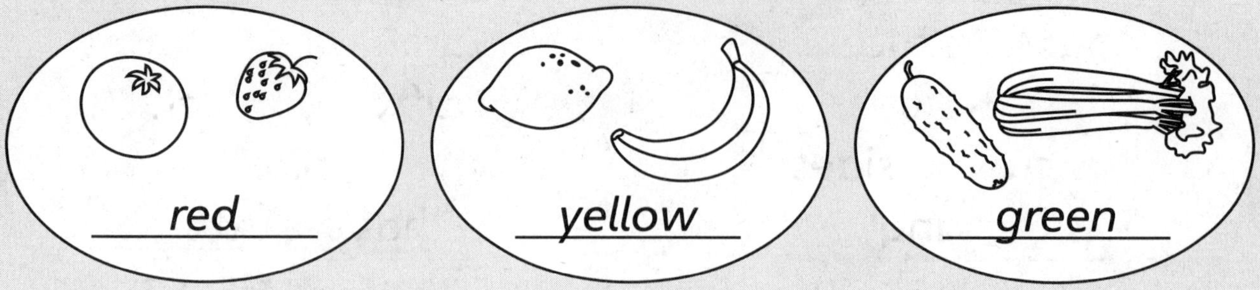

red

yellow

green

These are all __foods__. They are sorted by __colour__.

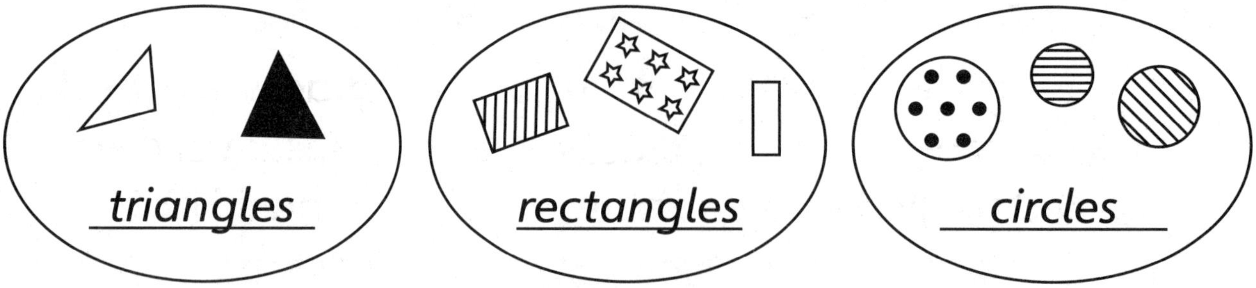

triangles

rectangles

circles

These are all _____. They are sorted by _____.

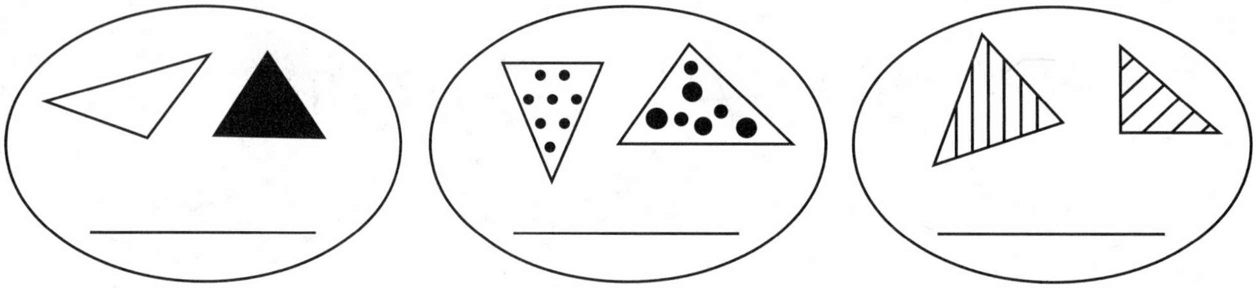

These are all _____. They are sorted by _____.

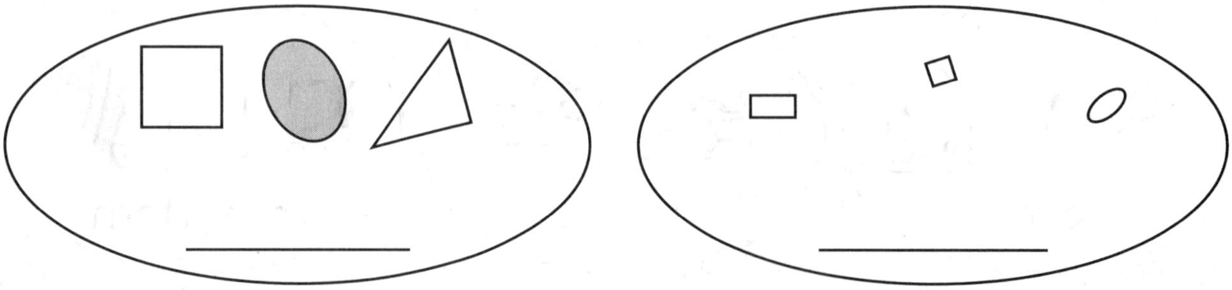

These are all _____. They are sorted by _____.

Probability and Data Management 2-4

| geometric properties | not geometric properties |
|---|---|
| has 4 vertices<br>has 6 sides<br>has curved sides<br>is a triangle<br>all sides are equal | large     dotted<br>fluffy     thick<br>pink<br>has a pattern<br>its name starts with "s" |

☐ Circle the geometric properties.

| | | |
|---|---|---|
| curly<br>has 5 sides<br>is a rectangle | small<br>pretty<br>blue | made of wood<br>has 3 vertices<br>has 7 dots |

☐ Write **geometric** or **not geometric**.

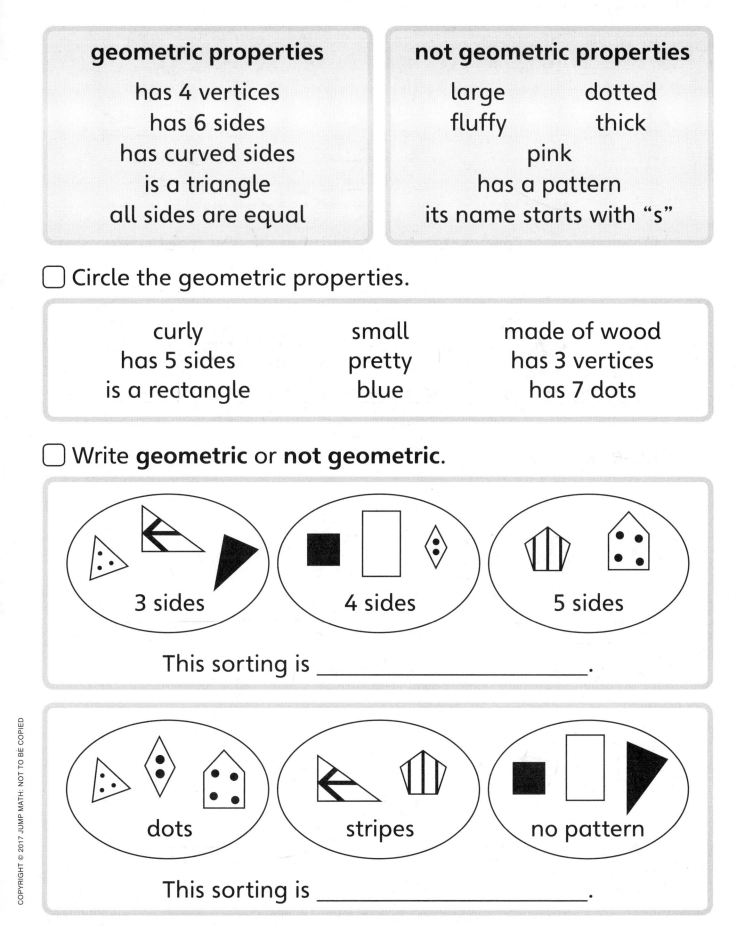

3 sides     4 sides     5 sides

This sorting is _____.

dots     stripes     no pattern

This sorting is _____.

# Sort and Graph

◯ Sort the data.
◯ Write the sorted data in the correct rows.

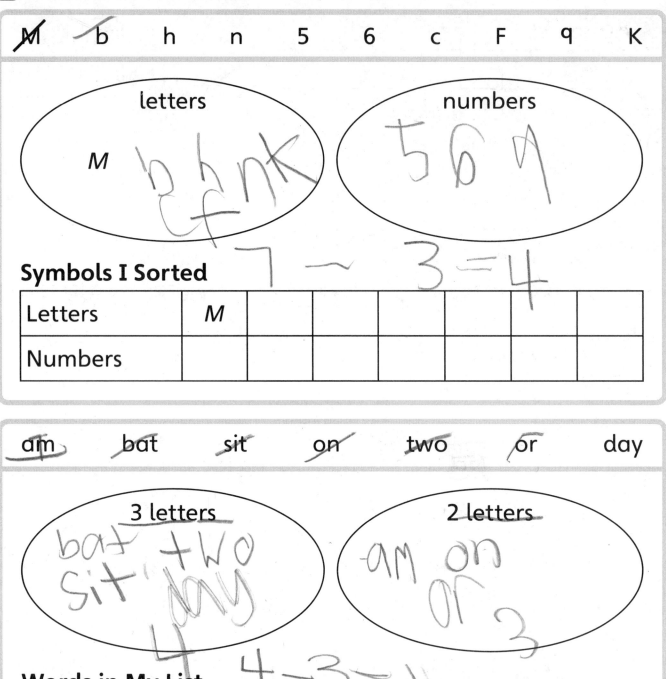

~~M~~    b    h    n    5    6    c    F    9    K

letters

M *bhnk*

numbers

*56 9*

*7 ~ 3 = 4*

**Symbols I Sorted**

| Letters | M |  |  |  |  |  |  |
|---------|---|--|--|--|--|--|--|
| Numbers |   |  |  |  |  |  |  |

~~am~~    ~~bat~~    ~~sit~~    ~~on~~    ~~two~~    ~~or~~    day

3 letters

*bat sit two day*

2 letters

*am on or*

*3*

*4*

*4 - 3 = 1*

**Words in My List**

| 3 letters |  |  |  |  |
|-----------|--|--|--|--|
| 2 letters |  |  |  |  |

# Pictographs

## Lunch Time

| At home | 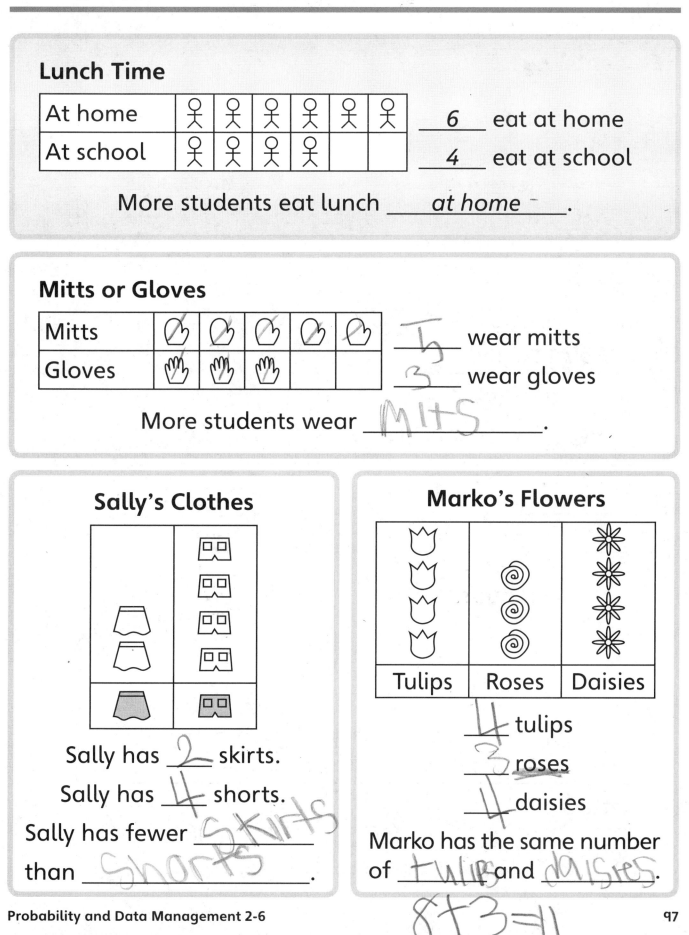 | | | | | | __6__ eat at home |
|---------|---|---|---|---|---|---|---|
| At school | | | | | | | __4__ eat at school |

More students eat lunch ___*at home*___.

## Mitts or Gloves

| Mitts | | | | | | __5__ wear mitts |
|-------|---|---|---|---|---|---|
| Gloves | | | | | | __3__ wear gloves |

More students wear ___MITS___.

## Sally's Clothes

Sally has __2__ skirts.

Sally has __4__ shorts.

Sally has fewer ___Skirts___

than ___Shorts___.

## Marko's Flowers

| Tulips | Roses | Daisies |
|--------|-------|---------|

__4__ tulips

__3__ roses

__4__ daisies

Marko has the same number

of ___tulips___ and ___daisies___.

8+3=11

How many more?

## Students' Ages

| 7-year-olds | 🧍 🧍 🧍 🧍 | | | | 4 | _7-year-olds_ |
|---|---|---|---|---|---|---|
| 8-year-olds | 🧍 🧍 🧍 🧍 🧍 🧍 🧍 | | 7 | | | _8-year-olds_ |

___7___ – ___4___ = ___3___ more

There are ___3___ more 8-year-olds than 7-year-olds.

## Shoes

| Running shoes | 🧍 🧍 🧍 🧍 🧍 🧍 🧍 🧍 | | | 7 | _____ |
|---|---|---|---|---|---|
| Boots | 🧍 🧍 🧍 🧍 | | | 4 | _____ |

___8___ – ___4___ = ___4___ fewer

___4___ fewer people wear boots than running shoes.

## Birds We Saw

| Pigeons | 🐦 🐦 🐦 | | | | 3 | _____ |
|---|---|---|---|---|---|---|
| Robins | 🐦 🐦 🐦 🐦 🐦 | | | 5 | | _____ |

___5___ – ___3___ = ___2___ fewer

We saw ___2___ fewer pigeons than robins.

## Pet Owners

| Have a pet | 🧍 🧍 🧍 🧍 🧍 🧍 🧍 🧍 🧍 | | 9 | _____ |
|---|---|---|---|---|
| Have no pet | 🧍 🧍 🧍 🧍 🧍 🧍 🧍 | | 7 | _____ |

___9___ – ___7___ = ___2___ more

___2___ more children have a pet than do not.

☐ Use the pictograph to fill in the blanks.

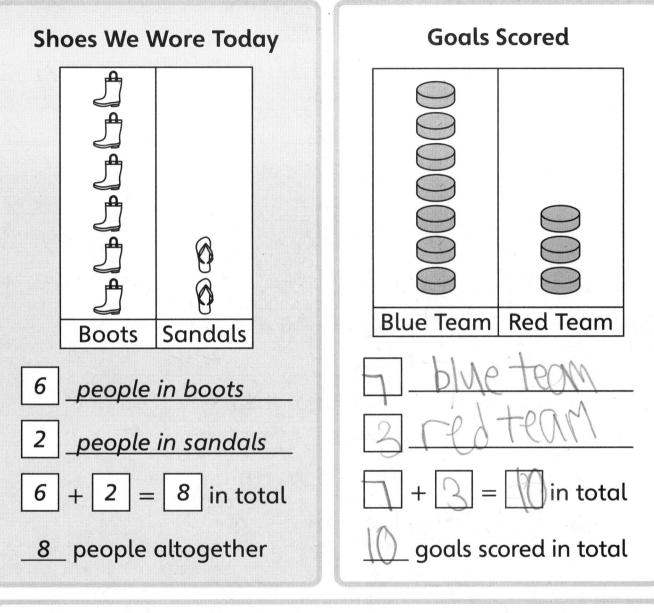

**Shoes We Wore Today**

| Boots | Sandals |
|-------|---------|

6 _people in boots_

2 _people in sandals_

6 + 2 = 8 in total

8 people altogether

**Goals Scored**

| Blue Team | Red Team |
|-----------|----------|

7 blue team

3 red team

7 + 3 = 10 in total

10 goals scored in total

**Favourite After-School Club**

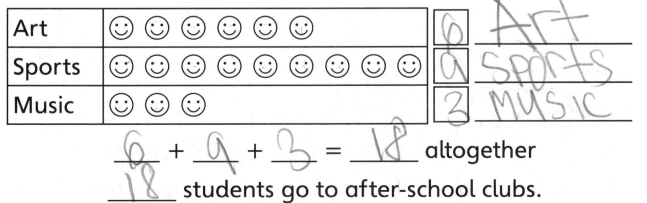

| Art | ☺ ☺ ☺ ☺ ☺ ☺ | 6 Art |
| Sports | ☺ ☺ ☺ ☺ ☺ ☺ ☺ ☺ ☺ | 9 Sports |
| Music | ☺ ☺ ☺ | 3 Music |

6 + 9 + 3 = 18 altogether

18 students go to after-school clubs.

# Drawing Pictographs

◯ Use the graphs to answer the questions.

**Lunch in Ms. Lee's Class**

| At school | S | S | S | S | S | S | S | | | | | | | 7 |
|-----------|---|---|---|---|---|---|---|---|---|---|---|---|---|---|
| At home | H | H | H | H | H | H | H | H | H | H | H | H | H | 13 |

More students in Ms. Lee's class eat lunch
_____at home_____ than _____at school_____.

**Lunch in Mr. King's Class**

| At school | S | S | | S | S | | S | S | | S | S | | | 8 |
|-----------|---|---|---|---|---|---|---|---|---|---|---|---|---|---|
| At home | H | H | H | H | H | H | | H | H | H | | | | 9 |

Mr. King's students think **more** of them eat at school than at home. Is that correct? _____NO_____

Fix the graph so that it is easier to read.

| At school | S | S | S | S | S | S | S | | | | | | |
|-----------|---|---|---|---|---|---|---|---|---|---|---|---|---|
| At home | h | h | h | h | h | h | h | | | | | | |

◯ Use data from the graphs above.

**Lunch at School**

| Ms. Lee's class | | | | | | | | | | | | | |
|-----------------|---|---|---|---|---|---|---|---|---|---|---|---|---|
| Mr. King's class | | | | | | | | | | | | | |

Which teacher has more students eating at school? _____

How many more? _____

**Probability and Data Management 2-7**

☐ Draw ☺ to show the data.
☐ Answer the questions.

*Difference (−)*
*all together +*

## Favourite Ball Games

| Soccer | ☺ | ☺ | ☺ | ☺ | ☺ | |
|---|---|---|---|---|---|---|
| Basketball | 0 | 0 | 0 | | | |
| Baseball | 0 | 0 | 0 | 0 | | |

5 like soccer the most.

3 like basketball the most.

4 like baseball the most.

How many more students like soccer the most than like baseball the most? *5 − 4 = 1*

## Shoes We Wear

*5 + 2 + 4 = 11*

| Running shoes | 5 | S | S | S | S |
|---|---|---|---|---|---|
| Boots | B | B | | | |
| Sandals | S | S | S | S | |

5 wear running shoes.

2 wear boots.

4 wear sandals.

How many fewer students wear boots than sandals? *2*

*4 − 2 = 2*

Kate asked friends where they will be during March break.

Title: _____

| Camp | |
|---|---|
| | |
| | |
| Do not know | |

5 will go to camp.

3 will stay at home.

2 will go to a cottage.

4 do not know.

How many friends did Kate ask? _____

☐ Write one thing you learned from Kate's graph.

# Counting to 100

How many crayons?

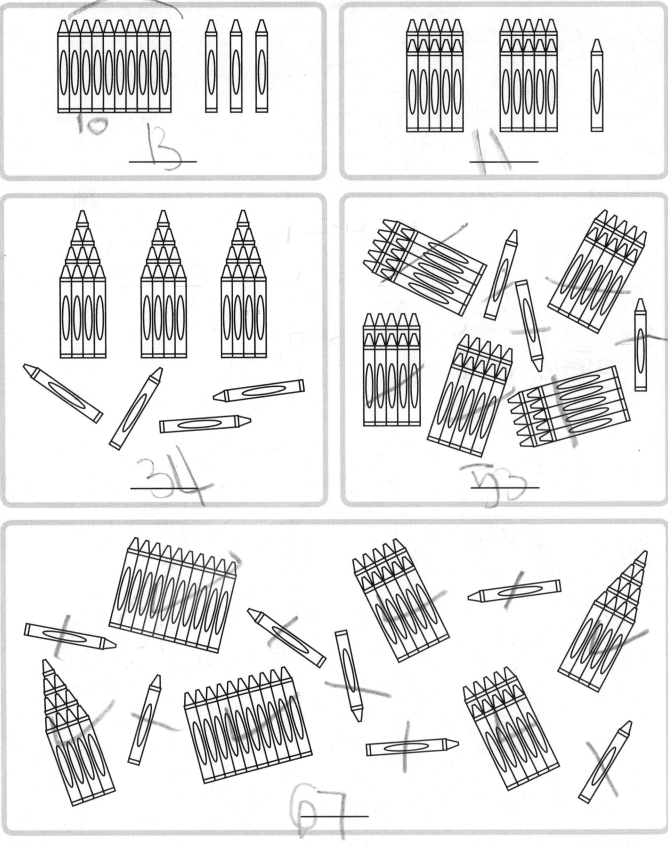

☐ Count the groups of tens and ones.
☐ Write the number.

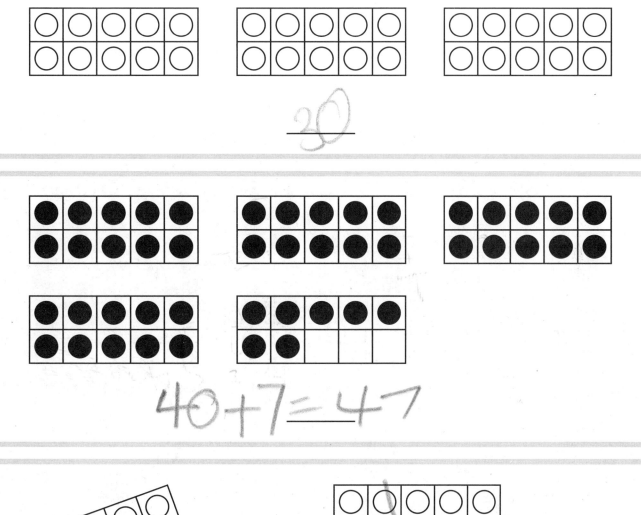

_30_

$40 + 7 = \underline{47}$

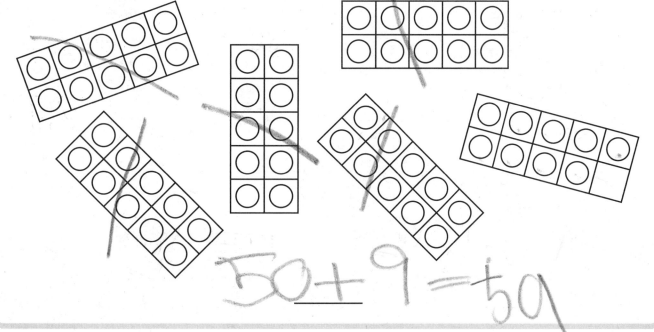

$50 + 9 = \underline{\phantom{00}} 59$

# Hundreds Charts

Sam is looking for numbers in the hundreds chart.

☐ Colour where he should start.

| | |
|---|---|
| Find 58 using grey. | Find 90 using green. |
| Find 87 using red. | Find 65 using yellow. |
| Find 62 using blue. | Find 71 using orange. |

| 1 | 2 | 3 | 4 | 5 | 6 | 7 | 8 | 9 | 10 |
|---|---|---|---|---|---|---|---|---|---|
| | | | | | | | | | |
| | | | | | | | | | |

☐ Shade the number in the chart.
☐ Write what comes next and what comes before.

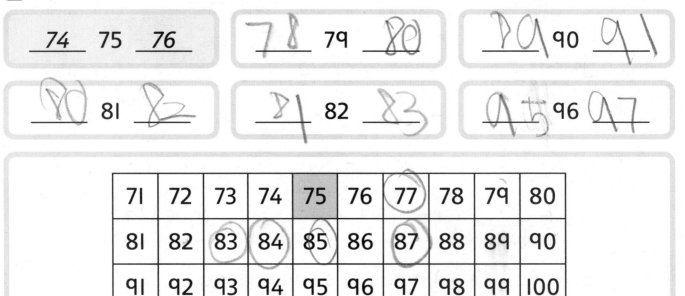

| 74 | 75 | 76 | | 78 | 79 | 80 | | 89 | 90 | 91 |
|---|---|---|---|---|---|---|---|---|---|---|

| 80 | 81 | 82 | | 81 | 82 | 83 | | 95 | 96 | 97 |
|---|---|---|---|---|---|---|---|---|---|---|

| 71 | 72 | 73 | 74 | 75 | 76 | 77 | 78 | 79 | 80 |
|---|---|---|---|---|---|---|---|---|---|---|
| 81 | 82 | 83 | 84 | 85 | 86 | 87 | 88 | 89 | 90 |
| 91 | 92 | 93 | 94 | 95 | 96 | 97 | 98 | 99 | 100 |

# More Tens and Ones Blocks

◯ Fill in the blanks.

| 1 | 2 | 3 | 4 | 5 | 6 | 7 | 8 | 9 | 10 |
|---|---|---|---|---|---|---|---|---|----|
| 11 | 12 | 13 | 14 | 15 | 16 | 17 | 18 | 19 | 20 |
| 21 | 22 | 23 | 24 | 25 | 26 | 27 | 28 | 29 | 30 |
| 31 | 32 | 33 | 34 | 35 | 36 | 37 | 38 | 39 | 40 |

32 =  ___3___ tens
    + ___2___ ones

| 1 | 2 | 3 | 4 | 5 | 6 | 7 | 8 | 9 | 10 |
|---|---|---|---|---|---|---|---|---|----|
| 11 | 12 | 13 | 14 | 15 | 16 | 17 | 18 | 19 | 20 |
| 21 | 22 | 23 | 24 | 25 | 26 | 27 | 28 | 29 | 30 |
| 31 | 32 | 33 | 34 | 35 | 36 | 37 | 38 | 39 | 40 |

34 =  ___3___ tens
    + ___4___ ones

◯ Place tens and ones blocks on the chart to show the number.
◯ Fill in the blanks.

| 1 | 2 | 3 | 4 | 5 | 6 | 7 | 8 | 9 | 10 |
|---|---|---|---|---|---|---|---|---|----|
| 11 | 12 | 13 | 14 | 15 | 16 | 17 | 18 | 19 | 20 |
| 21 | 22 | 23 | 24 | 25 | 26 | 27 | 28 | 29 | 30 |
| 31 | 32 | 33 | 34 | 35 | 36 | 37 | 38 | 39 | 40 |

28 is __2__ tens blocks and __8__ ones blocks.

27 is __2__ tens blocks and __7__ ones blocks.

23 is __2__ tens blocks and __3__ ones blocks.

35 is __3__ tens blocks and __5__ ones blocks.

30 is __3__ tens blocks and __0__ ones blocks.

✎ Lela says 32 and 23 mean the same thing.
   Is she correct? Explain.

◯ Fill in the table.
◯ Write the number.

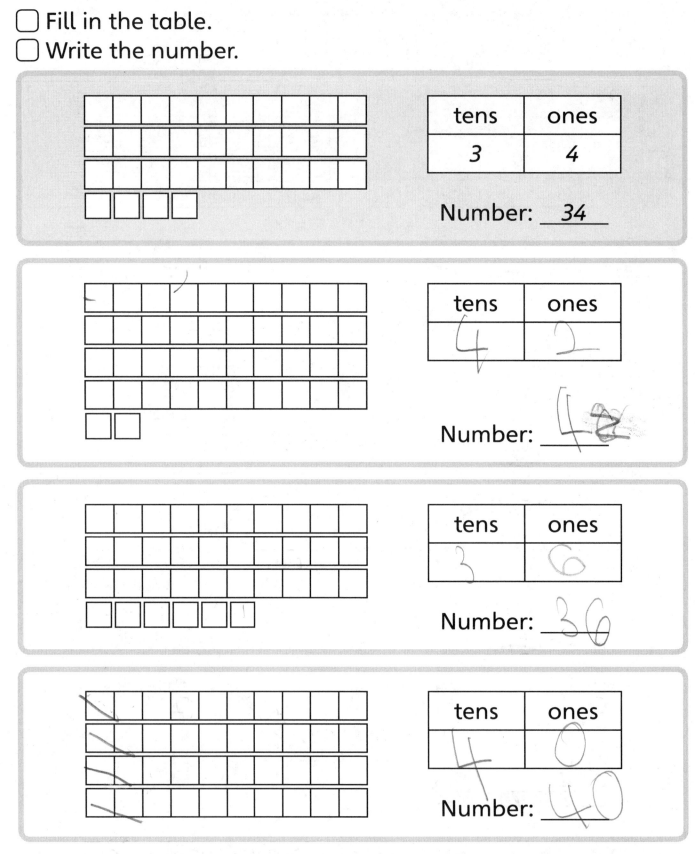

| tens | ones |
|------|------|
| 3 | 4 |

Number: __34__

| tens | ones |
|------|------|
| 4 | 2 |

Number: __42__

| tens | ones |
|------|------|
| 3 | 6 |

Number: __36__

| tens | ones |
|------|------|
| 4 | 0 |

Number: __40__

▤ Use blocks to show each number.    50   43   37   19   32

**Number Sense 2-20**

# How many ones altogether?

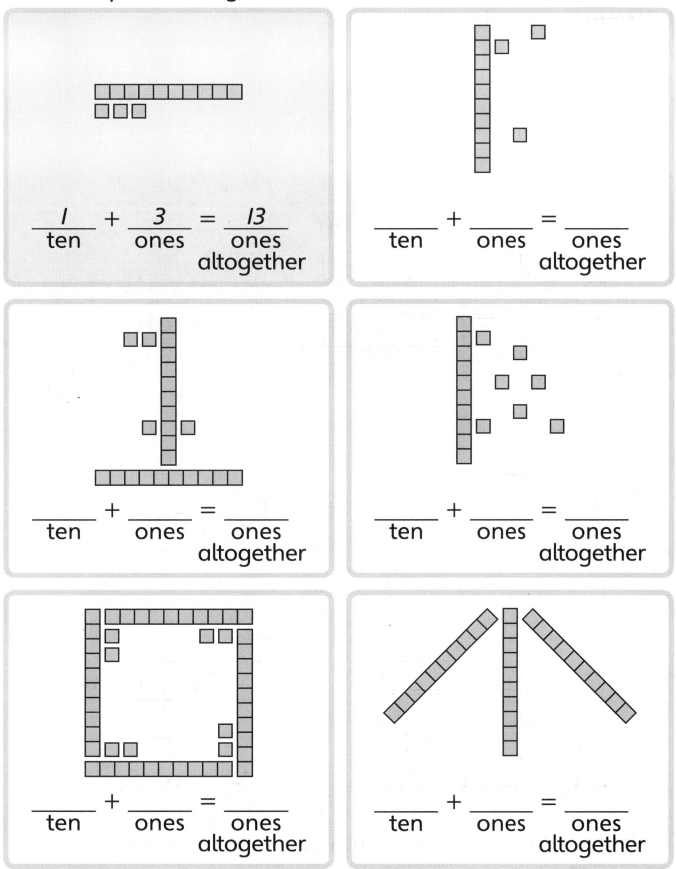

$\dfrac{1}{\text{ten}}$ + $\dfrac{3}{\text{ones}}$ = $\dfrac{13}{\substack{\text{ones} \\ \text{altogether}}}$

$\dfrac{\rule{2em}{0.4pt}}{\text{ten}}$ + $\dfrac{\rule{2em}{0.4pt}}{\text{ones}}$ = $\dfrac{\rule{2em}{0.4pt}}{\substack{\text{ones} \\ \text{altogether}}}$

$\dfrac{\rule{2em}{0.4pt}}{\text{ten}}$ + $\dfrac{\rule{2em}{0.4pt}}{\text{ones}}$ = $\dfrac{\rule{2em}{0.4pt}}{\substack{\text{ones} \\ \text{altogether}}}$

$\dfrac{\rule{2em}{0.4pt}}{\text{ten}}$ + $\dfrac{\rule{2em}{0.4pt}}{\text{ones}}$ = $\dfrac{\rule{2em}{0.4pt}}{\substack{\text{ones} \\ \text{altogether}}}$

$\dfrac{\rule{2em}{0.4pt}}{\text{ten}}$ + $\dfrac{\rule{2em}{0.4pt}}{\text{ones}}$ = $\dfrac{\rule{2em}{0.4pt}}{\substack{\text{ones} \\ \text{altogether}}}$

$\dfrac{\rule{2em}{0.4pt}}{\text{ten}}$ + $\dfrac{\rule{2em}{0.4pt}}{\text{ones}}$ = $\dfrac{\rule{2em}{0.4pt}}{\substack{\text{ones} \\ \text{altogether}}}$

# Ordering Numbers to I00

☐ Circle the largest number.

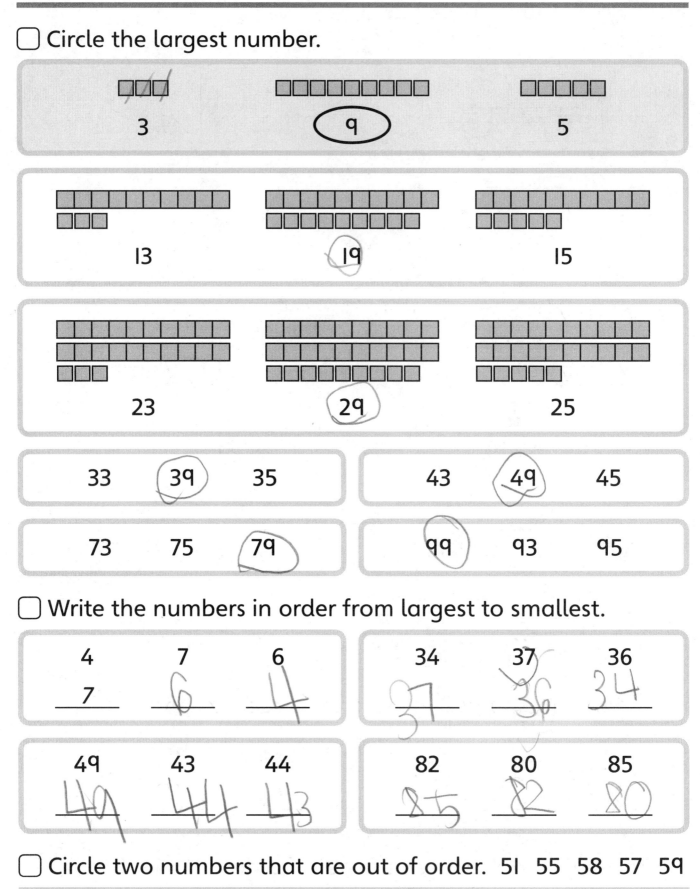

3    ⑨    5

13    ⑲    15

23    ㉙    25

33    ㊴    35          43    ㊾    45

73    75    ⑲          ⑨⑨    93    95

☐ Write the numbers in order from largest to smallest.

4    7    6          34    37    36
_7_  _6_  _4_        _37_  _36_  _34_

49    43    44          82    80    85
_49_  _44_  _43_        _85_  _82_  _80_

☐ Circle two numbers that are out of order.  5I  55  58  57  59

☐ Circle the largest number.

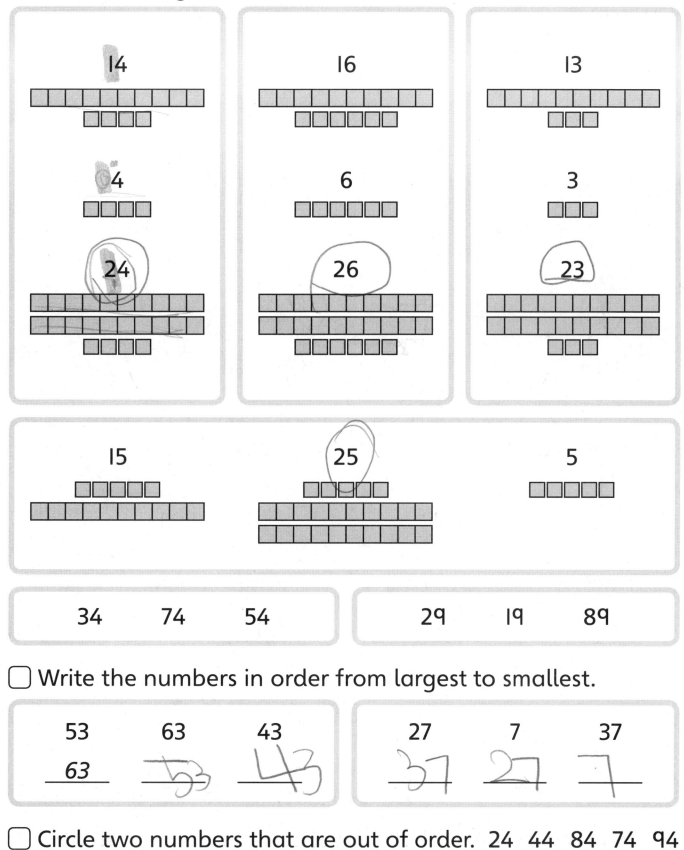

14

4

(24)

16

6

26

13

3

(23)

15

(25)

5

| 34 | 74 | 54 |

| 29 | 19 | 89 |

☐ Write the numbers in order from largest to smallest.

| 53 | 63 | 43 |
| 63 | 53 | 43 |

| 27 | 7 | 37 |
| 37 | 27 | 7 |

☐ Circle two numbers that are out of order.  24  44  84  74  94

## Circle the larger number.

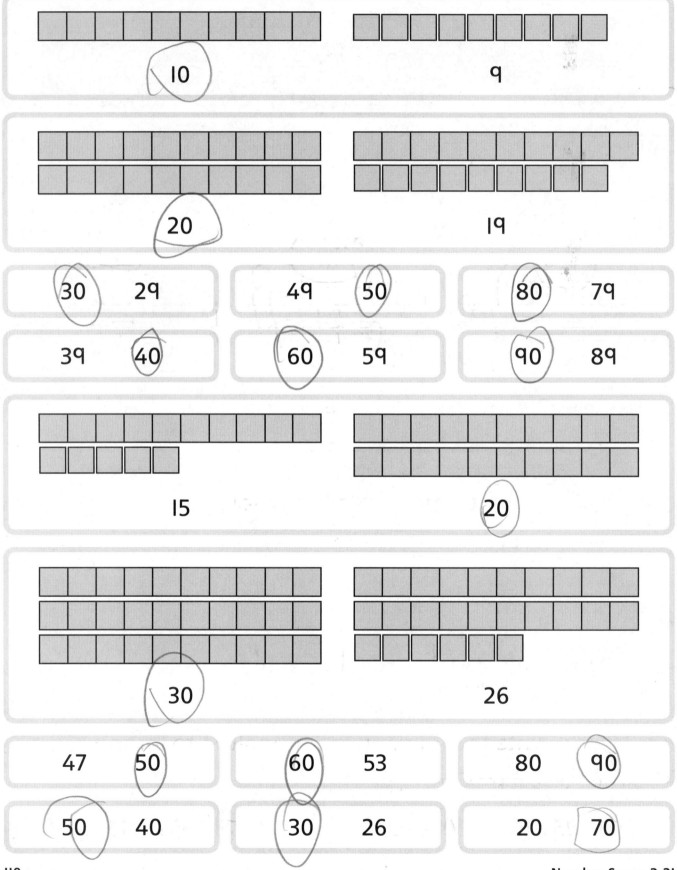

10       9

20      19

30   29     49   50     80   79

39   40     60   59     90   89

15      20

30      26

47   50     60   53     80   90

50   40     30   26     20   70

☐ Write the numbers in order.

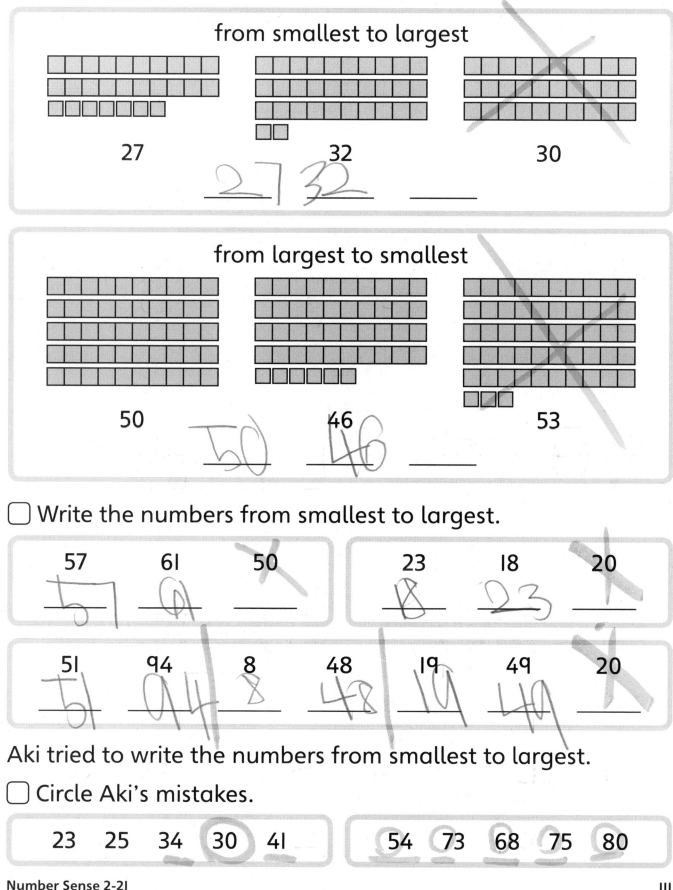

from smallest to largest

27          32          30

_27_  _32_  _____

from largest to smallest

50          46          53

_50_  _46_  _____

☐ Write the numbers from smallest to largest.

57     61     50

_57_  _61_  _____

23     18     20

_18_  _23_  _____

51     94     8     48     19     49     20

_51_  _94_  _8_  _48_  _19_  _49_  _____

Aki tried to write the numbers from smallest to largest.

☐ Circle Aki's mistakes.

23   25   34   30   41          54   73   68   75   80

☐ Circle the numbers on the number line.
☐ Write the numbers from smallest to largest.

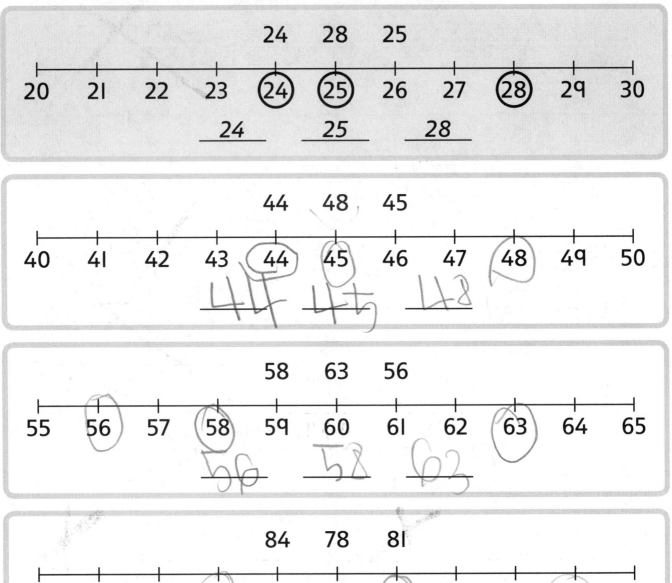

24    28    25

20   21   22   23   (24)  (25)  26   27   (28)  29   30

___24___   ___25___   ___28___

44    48    45

40   41   42   43   44   45   46   47   48   49   50

44    45    48

58    63    56

55   56   57   58   59   60   61   62   63   64   65

56    58    63

84    78    81

75   76   77   78   79   80   81   82   83   84   85

78    81    84

88    96    92    95    89

87   88   89   90   91   92   93   94   95   96   97

88    89    92    95    96

☐ Write the shaded numbers in order.
  Start with the smallest number.

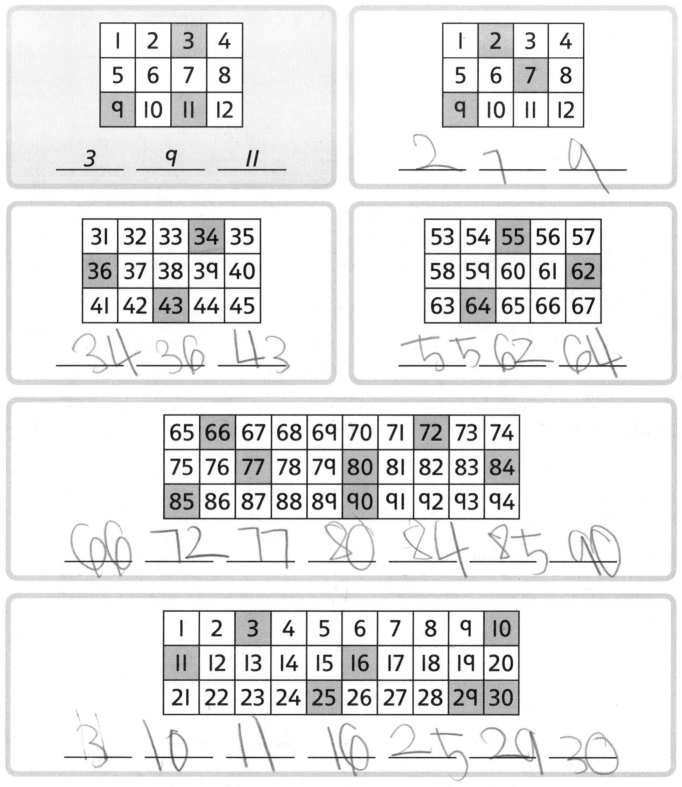

| 1 | 2 | 3 | 4 |
|---|---|---|---|
| 5 | 6 | 7 | 8 |
| 9 | 10 | 11 | 12 |

__3__ __9__ __11__

| 1 | 2 | 3 | 4 |
|---|---|---|---|
| 5 | 6 | 7 | 8 |
| 9 | 10 | 11 | 12 |

__2__ __7__ __9__

| 31 | 32 | 33 | 34 | 35 |
|----|----|----|----|----|
| 36 | 37 | 38 | 39 | 40 |
| 41 | 42 | 43 | 44 | 45 |

__34__ __36__ __43__

| 53 | 54 | 55 | 56 | 57 |
|----|----|----|----|----|
| 58 | 59 | 60 | 61 | 62 |
| 63 | 64 | 65 | 66 | 67 |

__55__ __62__ __64__

| 65 | 66 | 67 | 68 | 69 | 70 | 71 | 72 | 73 | 74 |
|----|----|----|----|----|----|----|----|----|----|
| 75 | 76 | 77 | 78 | 79 | 80 | 81 | 82 | 83 | 84 |
| 85 | 86 | 87 | 88 | 89 | 90 | 91 | 92 | 93 | 94 |

__66__ __72__ __77__ __80__ __84__ __85__ __90__

| 1 | 2 | 3 | 4 | 5 | 6 | 7 | 8 | 9 | 10 |
|---|---|---|---|---|---|---|---|---|----|
| 11 | 12 | 13 | 14 | 15 | 16 | 17 | 18 | 19 | 20 |
| 21 | 22 | 23 | 24 | 25 | 26 | 27 | 28 | 29 | 30 |

__3__ __10__ __11__ __16__ __25__ __29__ __30__

☐ Use a metre stick to check your answers.

# Adding, Subtracting, and Order

The dominoes got turned around.

☐ Write one addition sentence for both pictures.

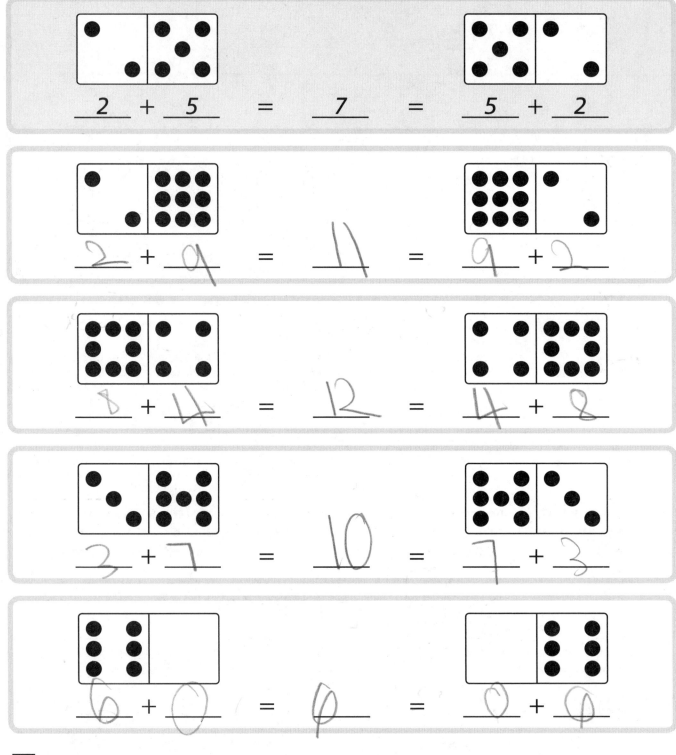

$\underline{2} + \underline{5} = \underline{7} = \underline{5} + \underline{2}$

$\underline{2} + \underline{9} = \underline{11} = \underline{9} + \underline{2}$

$\underline{8} + \underline{4} = \underline{12} = \underline{4} + \underline{8}$

$\underline{3} + \underline{7} = \underline{10} = \underline{7} + \underline{3}$

$\underline{6} + \underline{0} = \underline{6} = \underline{0} + \underline{6}$

📓 Randi says 34 + 17 = 17 + 34. Explain why she is correct.

# How many buttons altogether?

☐ Find the total in 6 different ways.

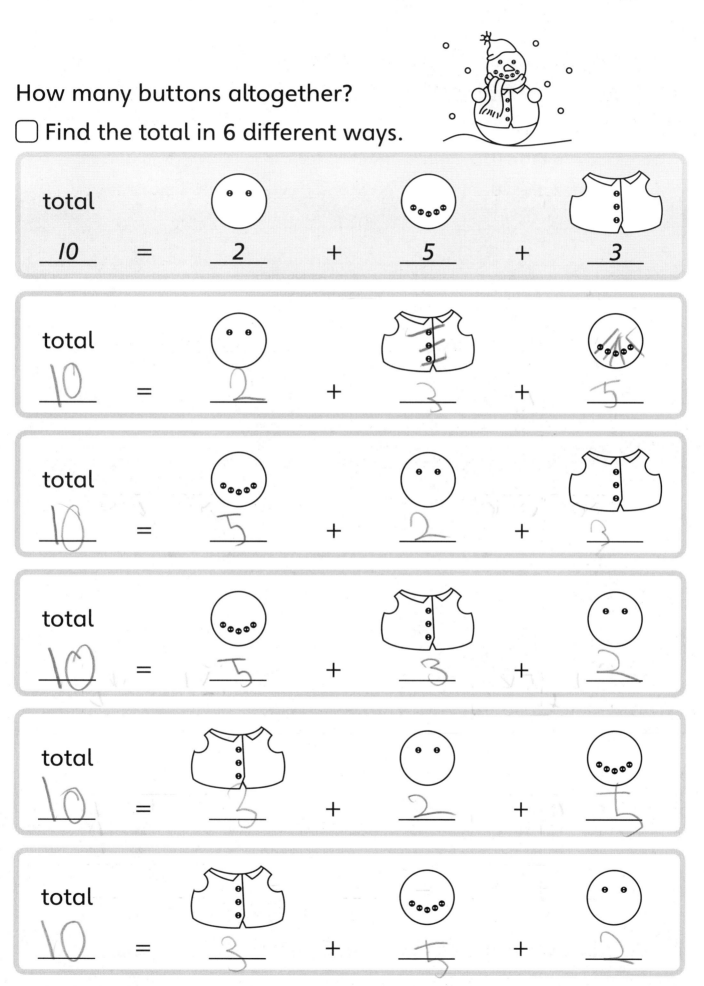

total

__10__ = __2__ + __5__ + __3__

total

__10__ = __2__ + __3__ + __5__

total

__10__ = __5__ + __2__ + __3__

total

__10__ = __5__ + __3__ + __2__

total

__10__ = __3__ + __2__ + __5__

total

__10__ = __3__ + __5__ + __2__

What does the subtraction mean?

☐ Use the picture to subtract.

5 − 2 means _____*take 2 away from 5*_____

○ ○ ○ ⊗ ⊗          5 − 2 = __3__

7 − 4 means _____

⊘ ⊘ ⊘ ⊘ ○ ○ ○          7 − 4 = __3__

8 − 3 means _____

⊘ ⊘ ⊘ ○ ○ ○ ○ ○          8 − 3 = __5__

☐ Can you take 5 away from 3? ○  ○  ○ yes / no
   Does 3 − 5 make sense? yes / no

☐ Solve the problem that makes sense.

3 − 6 = ___ or 6 − 3 = __3__     9 − 2 = __7__ or 2 − 9 = ___

4 − 8 = ___ or 8 − 4 = __4__     10 − 5 = __5__ or 5 − 10 = ___

📓 Which problem makes sense, 3 − 7 or 7 − 3? Explain.

**Number Sense 2-22**

# Adding with a Number Line

The frog takes 2 leaps. Where does it end up?

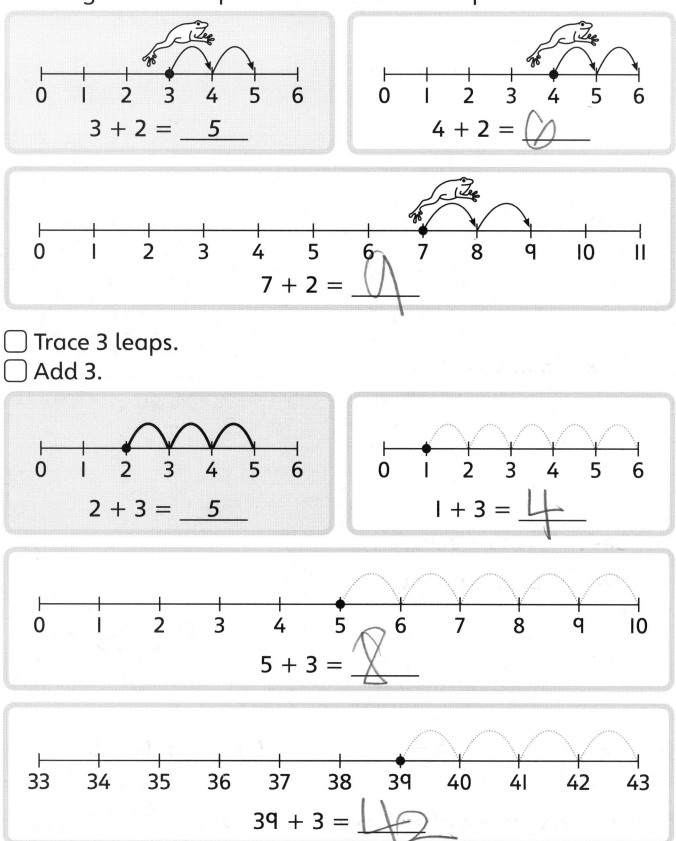

3 + 2 = __5__

4 + 2 = __6__

7 + 2 = __9__

☐ Trace 3 leaps.
☐ Add 3.

2 + 3 = __5__

1 + 3 = __4__

5 + 3 = __8__

39 + 3 = __42__

# The frog starts at the first number.

⬜ Draw a dot where the frog starts.

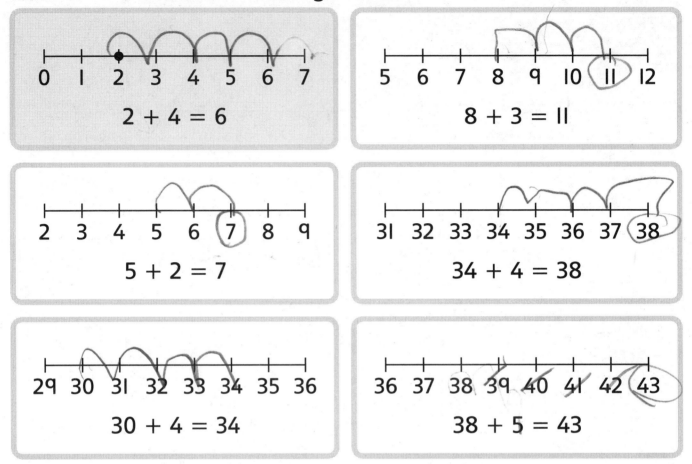

2 + 4 = 6

8 + 3 = 11

5 + 2 = 7

34 + 4 = 38

30 + 4 = 34

38 + 5 = 43

# The frog jumps the second number of leaps.
⬜ Draw the frog's leaps.

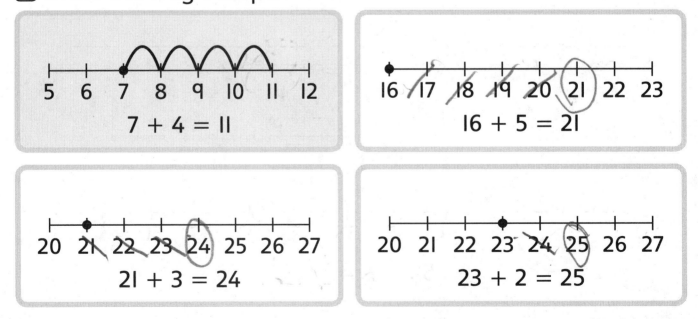

7 + 4 = 11

16 + 5 = 21

21 + 3 = 24

23 + 2 = 25

Use the number line to add.

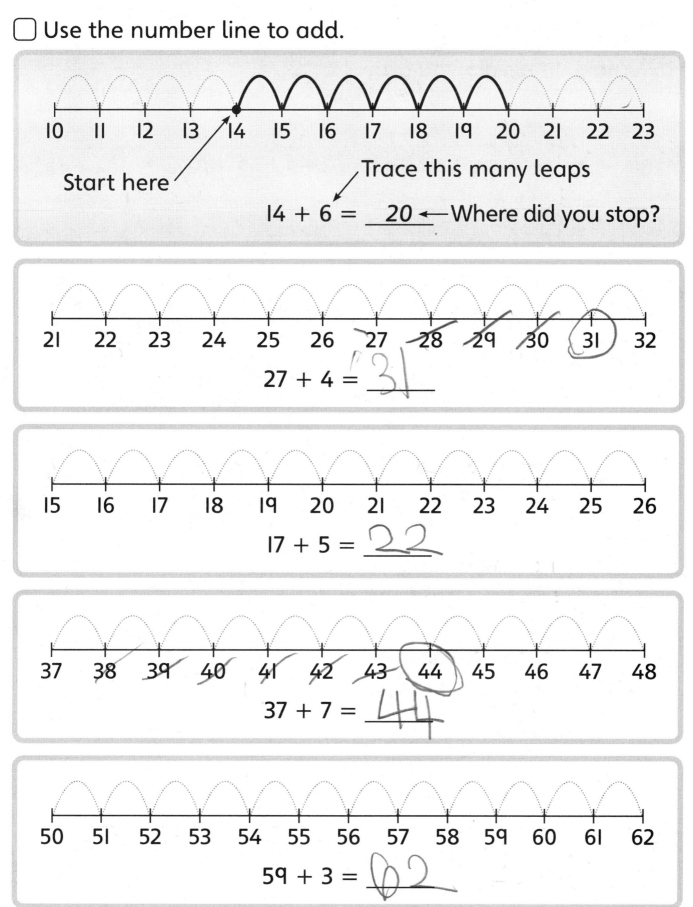

Start here

Trace this many leaps

$14 + 6 =$ __20__ ← Where did you stop?

$27 + 4 =$ __31__

$17 + 5 =$ __22__

$37 + 7 =$ __44__

$59 + 3 =$ __62__

Draw the leaps from the first dot to the second dot.
How many leaps did you draw?

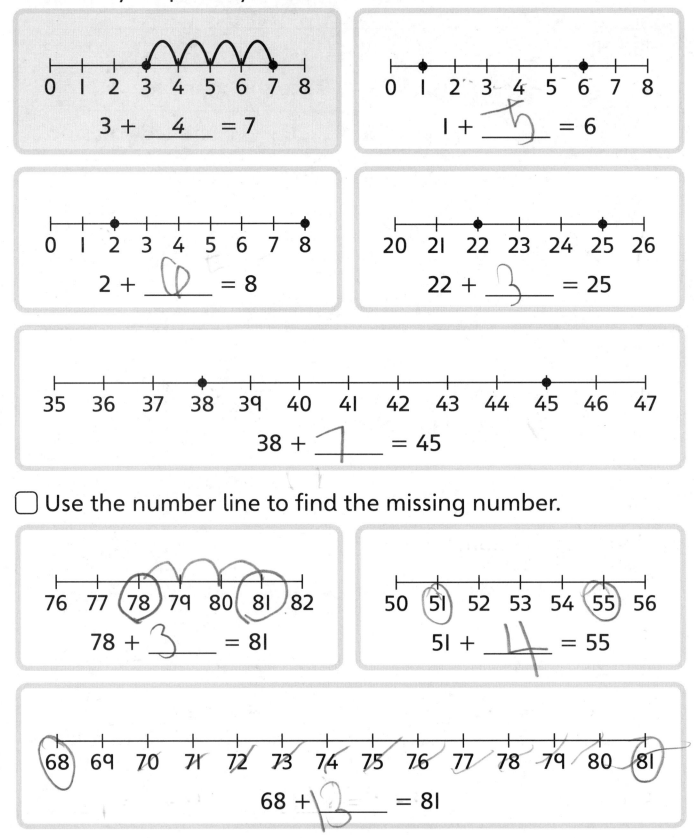

$3 + \underline{\ 4\ } = 7$

$1 + \underline{\ 5\ } = 6$

$2 + \underline{\ 6\ } = 8$

$22 + \underline{\ 3\ } = 25$

$38 + \underline{\ 7\ } = 45$

Use the number line to find the missing number.

$78 + \underline{\ 3\ } = 81$

$51 + \underline{\ 4\ } = 55$

$68 + \underline{\ 13\ } = 81$

Number Sense 2-23

# Adding by Counting On

☐ Colour the next circle.
☐ Add 1.

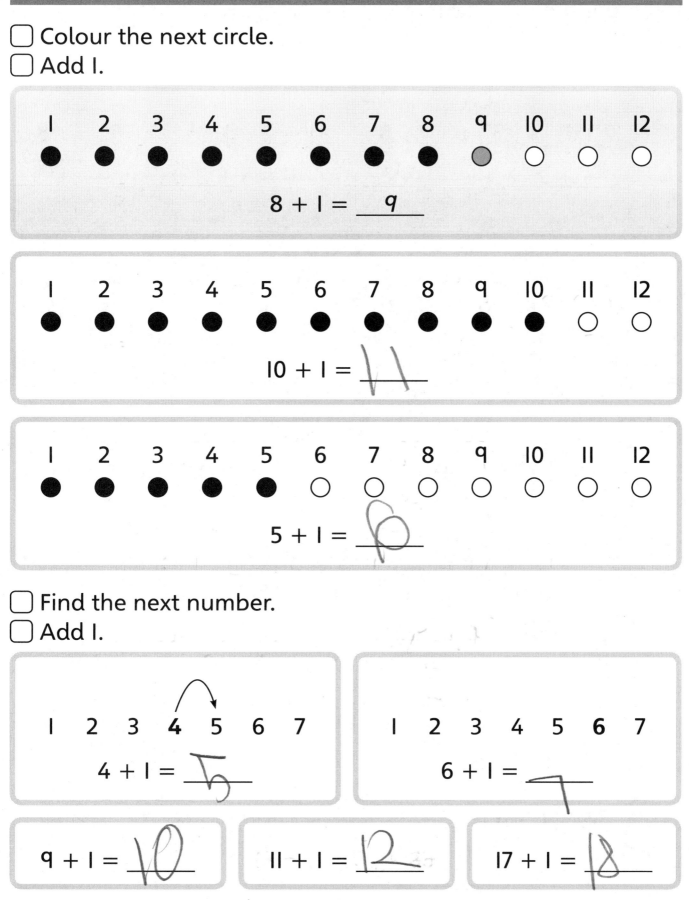

|  | 1 | 2 | 3 | 4 | 5 | 6 | 7 | 8 | 9 | 10 | 11 | 12 |

8 + 1 = __9__

10 + 1 = __11__

5 + 1 = __6__

☐ Find the next number.
☐ Add 1.

1  2  3  **4**  5  6  7

4 + 1 = __5__

1  2  3  4  5  **6**  7

6 + 1 = __7__

9 + 1 = __10__

11 + 1 = __12__

17 + 1 = __18__

☐ Find the next 2 numbers.
☐ Add 2.

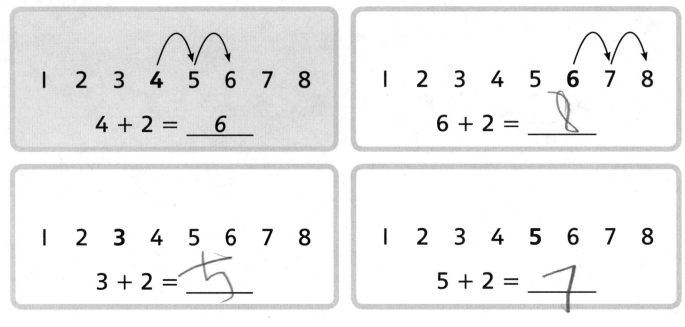

1  2  3  **4**  5  6  7  8

4 + 2 = __6__

1  2  3  4  5  **6**  7  8

6 + 2 = __8__

1  2  **3**  4  5  6  7  8

3 + 2 = __5__

1  2  3  4  **5**  6  7  8

5 + 2 = __7__

☐ Write the next 2 numbers to add 2.

7  __8__  __9__   so 7 + 2 = __9__

15  __16__  __17__   so 15 + 2 = __17__

89  __90__  __91__   so 89 + 2 = __91__

☐ Write the next 5 numbers to add 5.

2  __3__  __4__  __5__  __6__  __7__   so 2 + 5 = __7__

18  __19__  __20__  __21__  __22__  __23__   so 18 + 5 = __23__

☐ Start at the first number.
☐ Trace the second number of blanks.
☐ Add by counting on.

| 5 | _6_ | _7_ | _8_ | _9_ | _10_ | _11_ | ⋯⋯ | 5 + 6 = _11_ |

| 8 | 9 | 10 | | | | | | 8 + 2 = 10 |

| 21 | 22 | 23 | 24 | 25 | | | | 21 + 4 = 25 |

☐ Use your fingers to add by counting on.

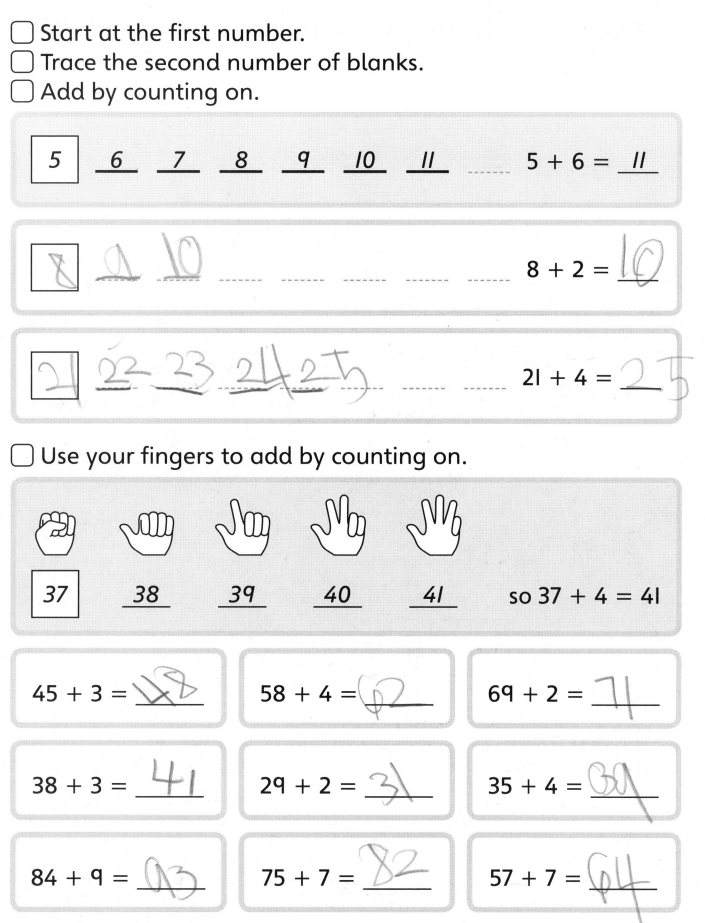

| 37 | _38_ | _39_ | _40_ | _41_ | so 37 + 4 = 41 |

45 + 3 = 48    58 + 4 = 62    69 + 2 = 71

38 + 3 = 41    29 + 2 = 31    35 + 4 = 39

84 + 9 = 93    75 + 7 = 82    57 + 7 = 64

□ Trace the correct number of blanks.
□ Add by counting on in 2 ways.

$7 + 3 =$ __10__

7 __8__ __9__ __10__

3 __4__ __5__ __6__ __7__ __8__ __9__ __10__

---

$2 + 5 =$ __7__

2

5

---

$9 + 3 =$ __12__

9

3

---

$4 + 8 =$ __12__

4

8

---

□ What is easier, counting on from the **bigger** number or from the **smaller** number? Explain.

_____

_____

_____

# Subtracting with a Number Line

The frog takes 2 leaps back. Where does it end up?

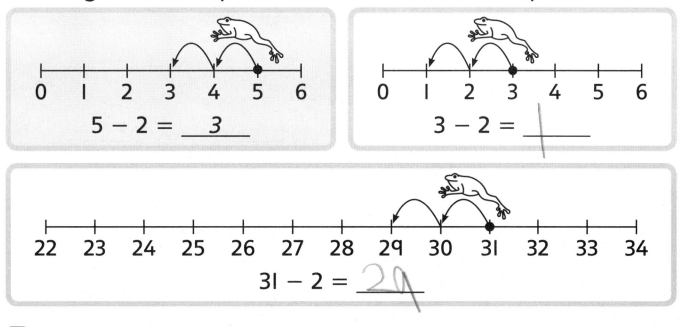

$5 - 2 = \underline{\quad 3 \quad}$

$3 - 2 = \underline{\quad 1 \quad}$

$31 - 2 = \underline{\quad 29 \quad}$

☐ Trace 3 leaps back.
☐ Subtract 3.

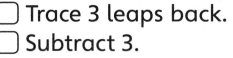

$4 - 3 = \underline{\quad 1 \quad}$

$6 - 3 = \underline{\quad 3 \quad}$

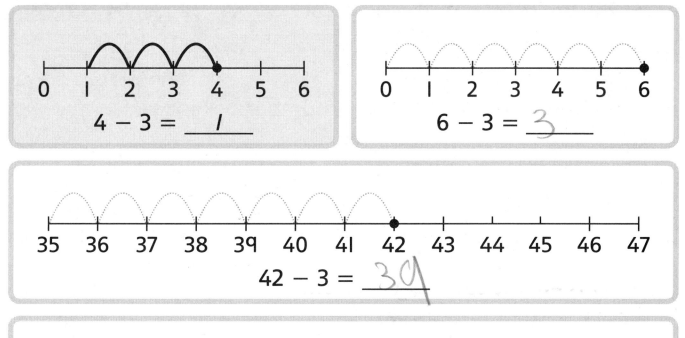

$42 - 3 = \underline{\quad 39 \quad}$

$94 - 3 = \underline{\quad 91 \quad}$

The frog starts at the first number.

☐ Draw a dot where the frog starts.

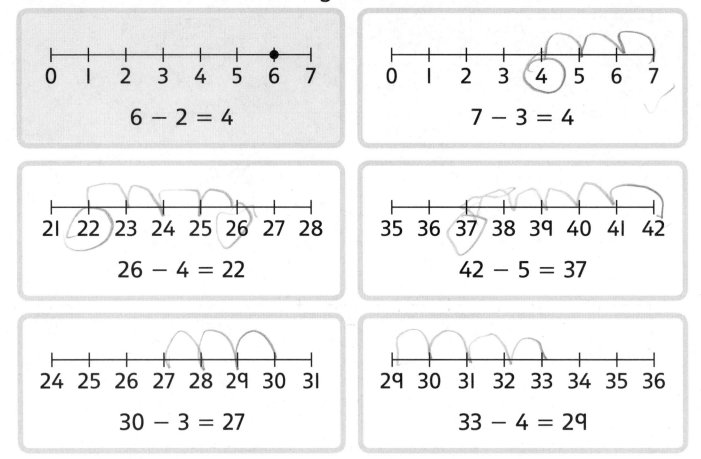

6 − 2 = 4

7 − 3 = 4

26 − 4 = 22

42 − 5 = 37

30 − 3 = 27

33 − 4 = 29

The frog jumps back the second number of leaps.

☐ Draw the frog's leaps.

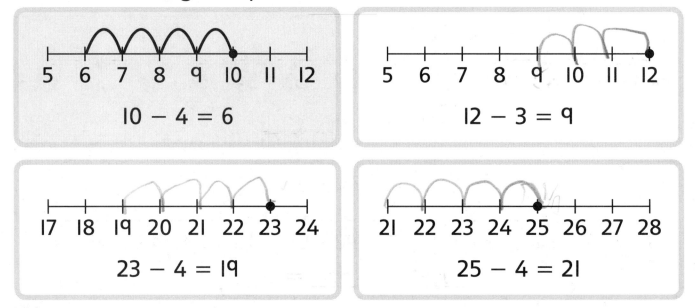

10 − 4 = 6

12 − 3 = 9

23 − 4 = 19

25 − 4 = 21

## ☐ Use the number line to subtract.

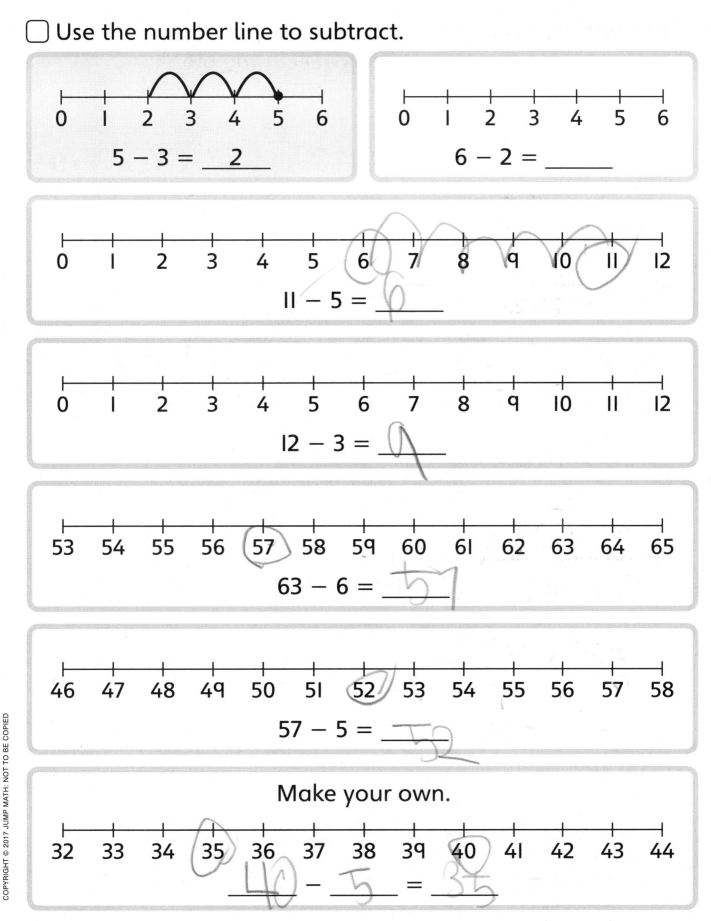

$5 - 3 =$ __2__

$6 - 2 =$ _____

$11 - 5 =$ __6__

$12 - 3 =$ __9__

$63 - 6 =$ __57__

$57 - 5 =$ __52__

### Make your own.

__40__ − __5__ = __35__

Draw the leaps from the second dot to the first dot.
How many leaps did you draw? Fill in the blank.

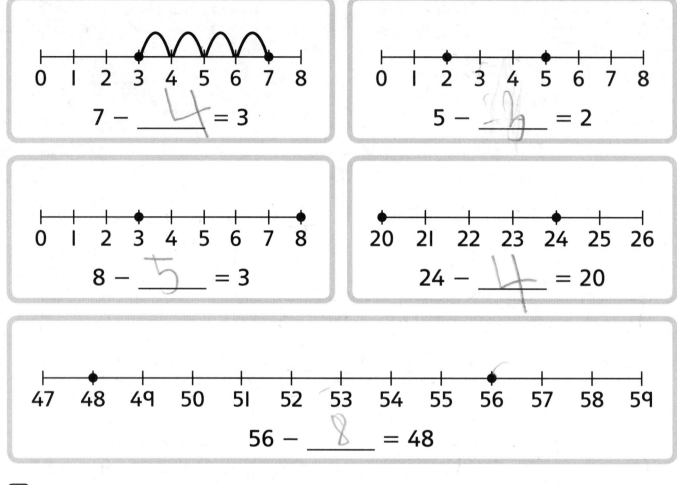

$7 - 4 = 3$

$5 - 3 = 2$

$8 - 5 = 3$

$24 - 4 = 20$

$56 - 8 = 48$

Use the number line to find the missing number.

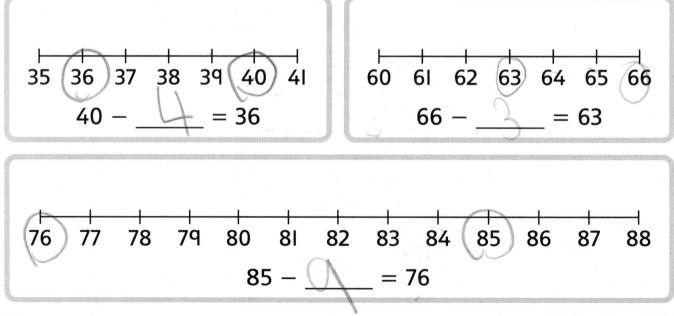

$40 - 4 = 36$

$66 - 3 = 63$

$85 - 9 = 76$

☐ Use the number line to add or subtract.

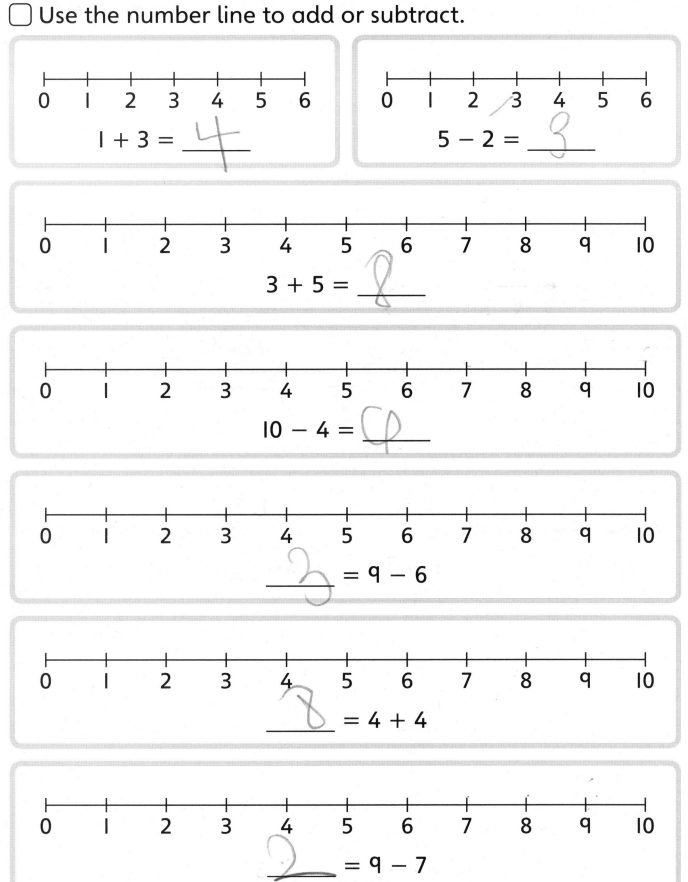

$1 + 3 = \underline{4}$

$5 - 2 = \underline{3}$

$3 + 5 = \underline{8}$

$10 - 4 = \underline{6}$

$\underline{3} = 9 - 6$

$\underline{8} = 4 + 4$

$\underline{2} = 9 - 7$

# Subtracting by Counting Backwards

☐ Subtract by counting back.

| 8 | 7 | 6 | 5 | 4 | 3 | 8 − 5 = 3 |

6    5    4    3    2       6 − 4 = 2

28    27    26    25       28 − 3 = 25

32    31    30    29    28    27     32 − 5 = 27

☐ Trace the blanks, then subtract.

21    20    19       21 − 2 = 19

30    29    28    27    26    25     30 − 5 = 25

43    42    41    40    39     43 − 4 = 39

☐ Keep track on your fingers to subtract.

28 − 4 = 24      32 − 3 = 29      41 − 2 = 39

# Subtracting by Counting On

☐ Subtract by counting forwards.

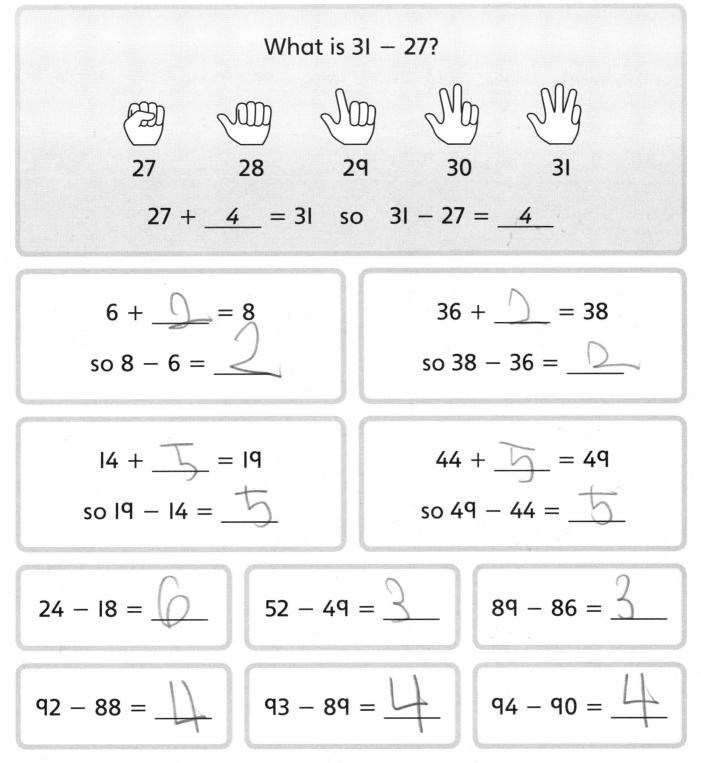

What is 31 − 27?

27        28        29        30        31

27 + __4__ = 31    so    31 − 27 = __4__

6 + __2__ = 8

so 8 − 6 = __2__

36 + __2__ = 38

so 38 − 36 = __2__

14 + __5__ = 19

so 19 − 14 = __5__

44 + __5__ = 49

so 49 − 44 = __5__

24 − 18 = __6__

52 − 49 = __3__

89 − 86 = __3__

92 − 88 = __4__

93 − 89 = __4__

94 − 90 = __4__

☐ Make up 3 subtraction questions. Solve them by counting forwards.

Subtract by counting forwards or backwards.

47 − 4 = _43_

39 − 36 = _3_

42 − 38 = _4_

31 − 6 = _25_

32 − 25 = _7_

33 − 29 = _4_

33 − 4 = _29_

45 − 7 = _38_

41 − 39 = _2_

21 − 15 = _6_

21 − 3 = _18_

46 − 8 = _38_

42 − 36 = _6_

42 − 5 = _37_

37 − 35 = _2_

24 − 3 = _21_

24 − 19 = _5_

37 − 4 = _33_

47 − 5 = _42_

47 − 2 = _45_

47 − 43 = _4_

Did you use counting forwards or backwards for the last question? Why?

Make up 3 subtraction questions. Solve them by counting backwards.

# Matching Shapes

☐ ✓ what is true and ✗ what is not true.

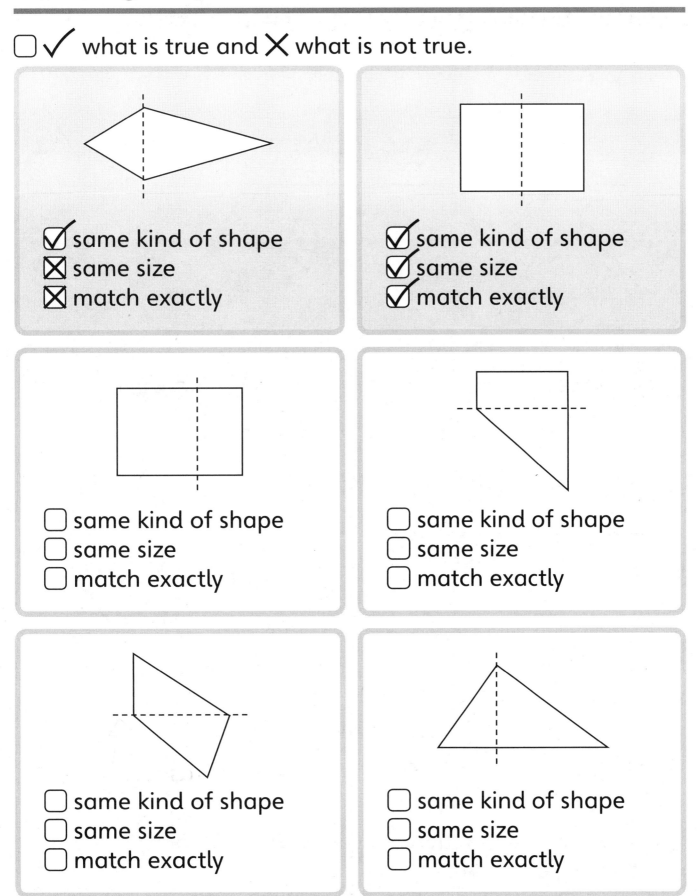

☑ same kind of shape
☒ same size
☒ match exactly

☑ same kind of shape
☑ same size
☑ match exactly

☐ same kind of shape
☐ same size
☐ match exactly

☐ same kind of shape
☐ same size
☐ match exactly

☐ same kind of shape
☐ same size
☐ match exactly

☐ same kind of shape
☐ same size
☐ match exactly

☐ Put an ✗ on the parts that **do not** match exactly.

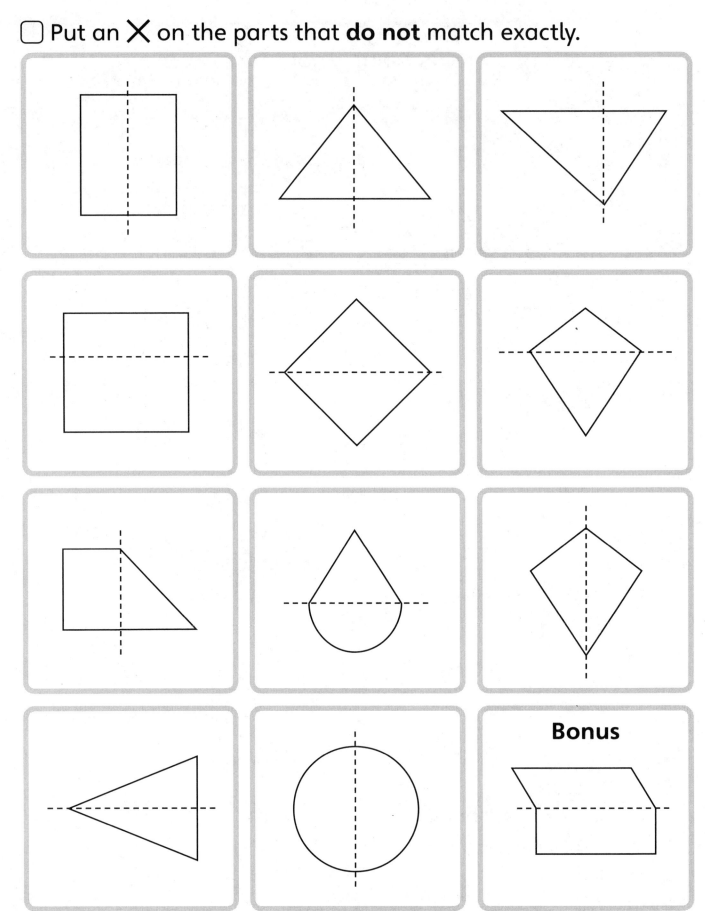

**Bonus**

# Lines of Symmetry

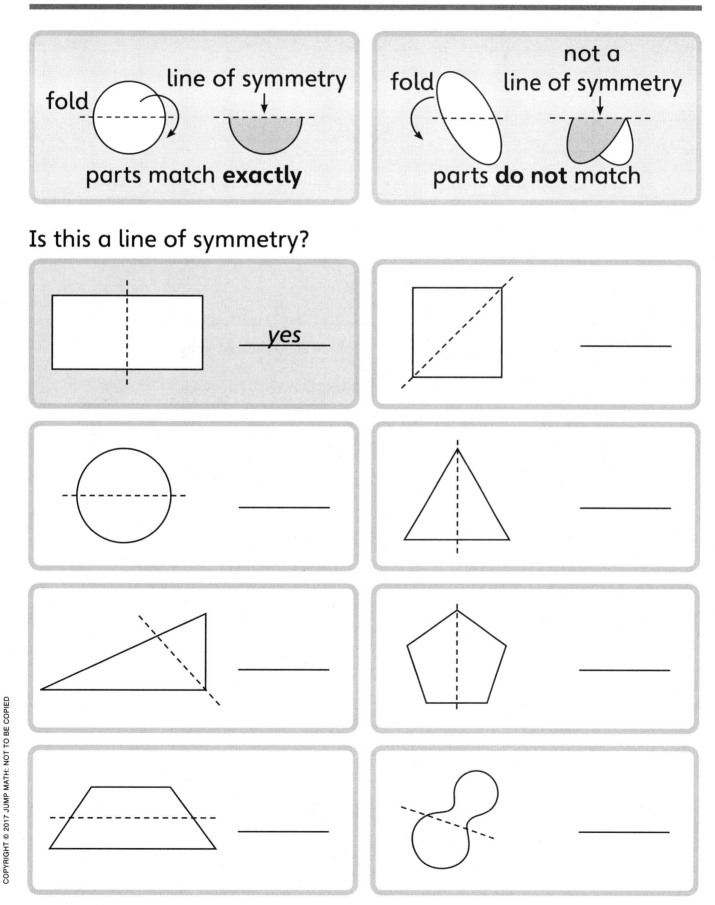

fold  line of symmetry
parts match **exactly**

fold  not a line of symmetry
parts **do not** match

Is this a line of symmetry?

_yes_

## ☐ Draw a line of symmetry.

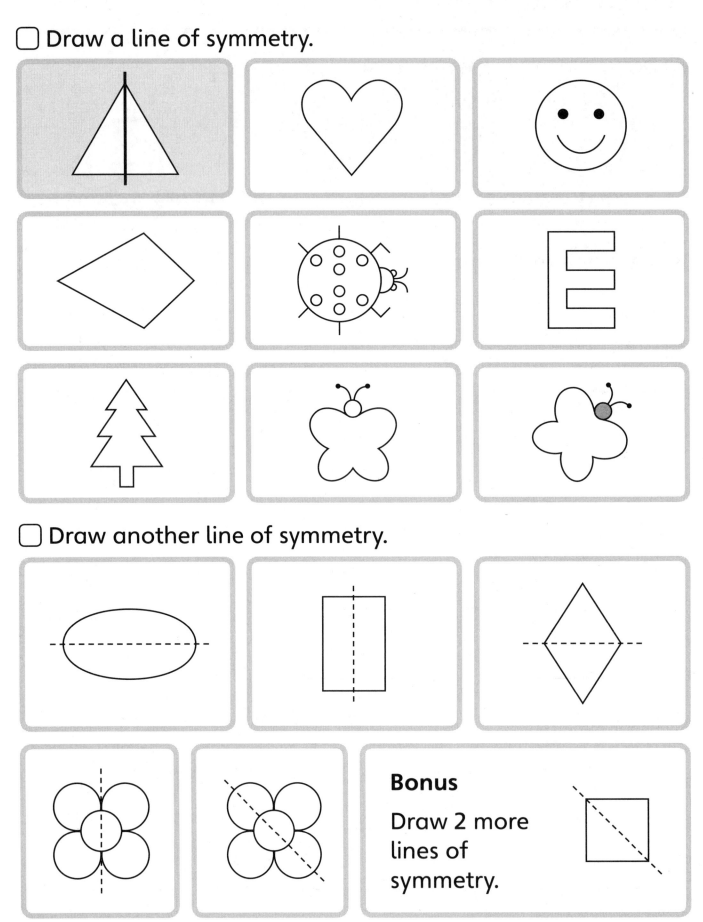

## ☐ Draw another line of symmetry.

**Bonus**

Draw 2 more lines of symmetry.

**Geometry 2-10**

# Does this shape have a line of symmetry?

⬚ Draw the lines of symmetry you find.

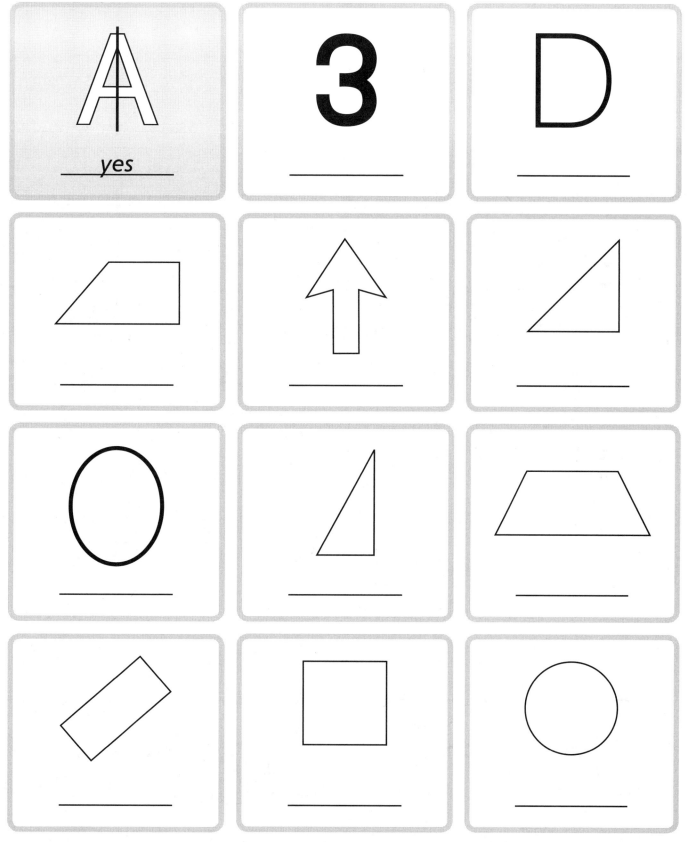

A    _yes_

3    _____

D    _____

_____

_____

_____

_____

_____

_____

_____

_____

_____

# Creating Symmetrical Shapes

☐ Draw the matching part of the symmetrical shape.

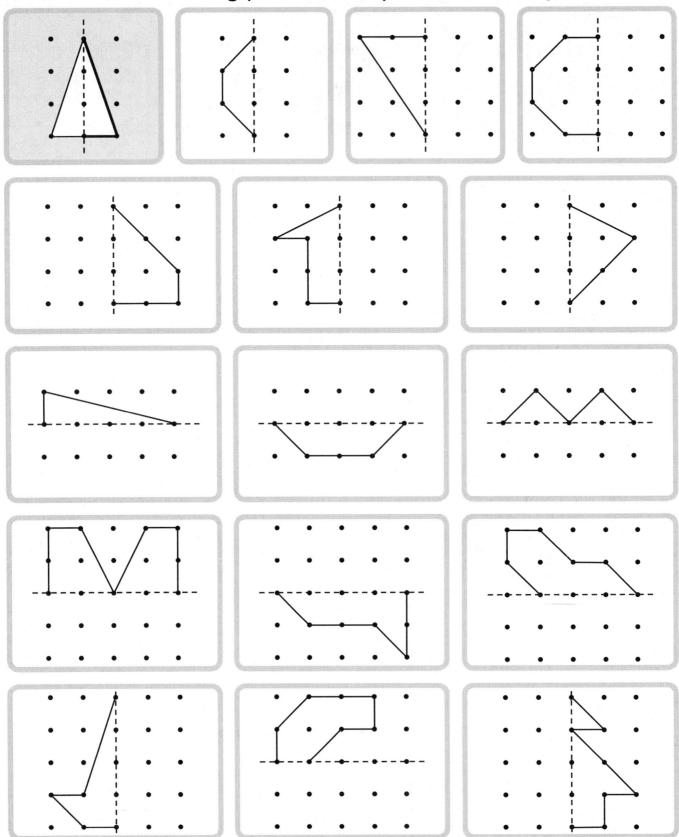

# Breaking and Creating Shapes

☐ Draw lines to make the shapes.

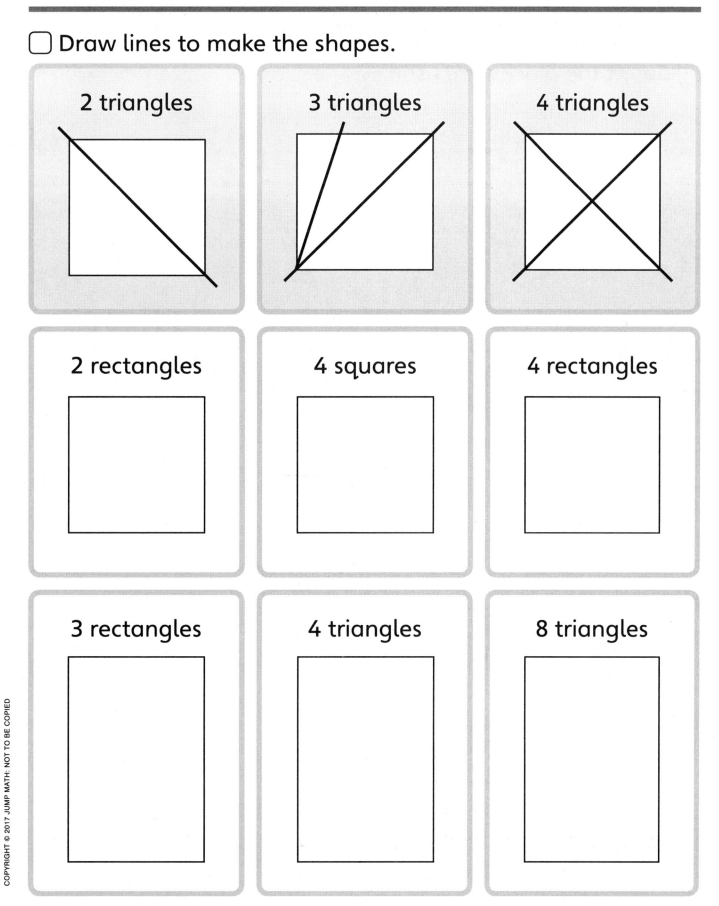

# Making Polygons

☐ Cover the bird with pattern blocks. Use different shapes.
☐ Count the blocks you used.

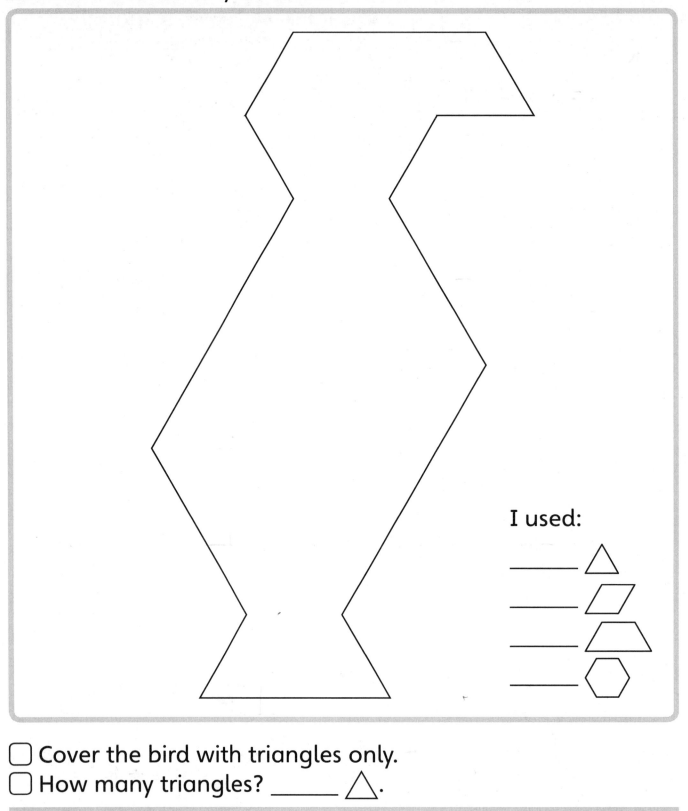

I used:

_____ △

_____ ▱

_____ ⬡

_____ ⬡

☐ Cover the bird with triangles only.
☐ How many triangles? _____ △.

# Equal and Not Equal

○ Add.

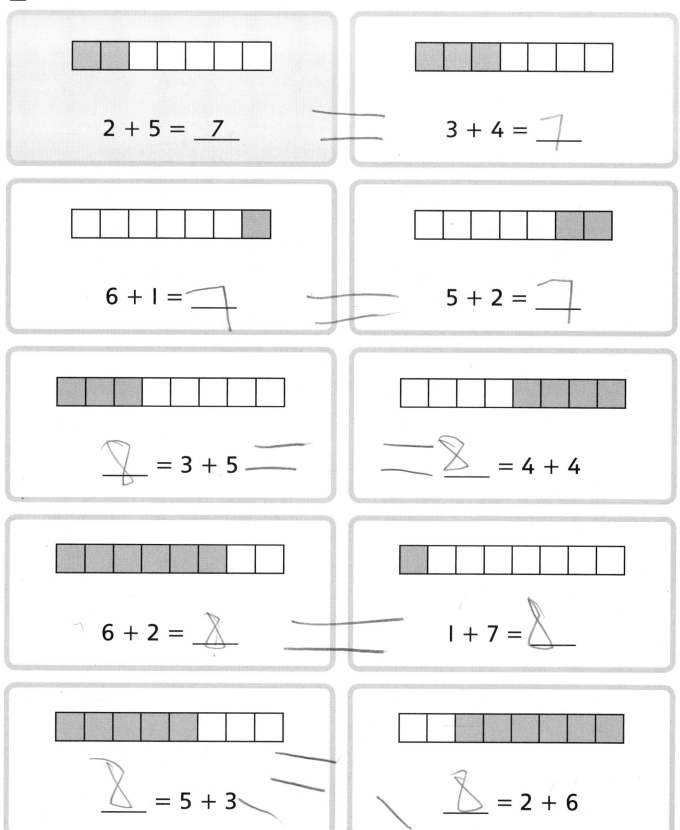

$2 + 5 = \underline{\ 7\ }$

$3 + 4 = \underline{\ 7\ }$

$6 + 1 = \underline{\ 7\ }$

$5 + 2 = \underline{\ 7\ }$

$\underline{\ 8\ } = 3 + 5$

$\underline{\ 8\ } = 4 + 4$

$6 + 2 = \underline{\ 8\ }$

$1 + 7 = \underline{\ 8\ }$

$\underline{\ 8\ } = 5 + 3$

$\underline{\ 8\ } = 2 + 6$

☐ Use the model to subtract.

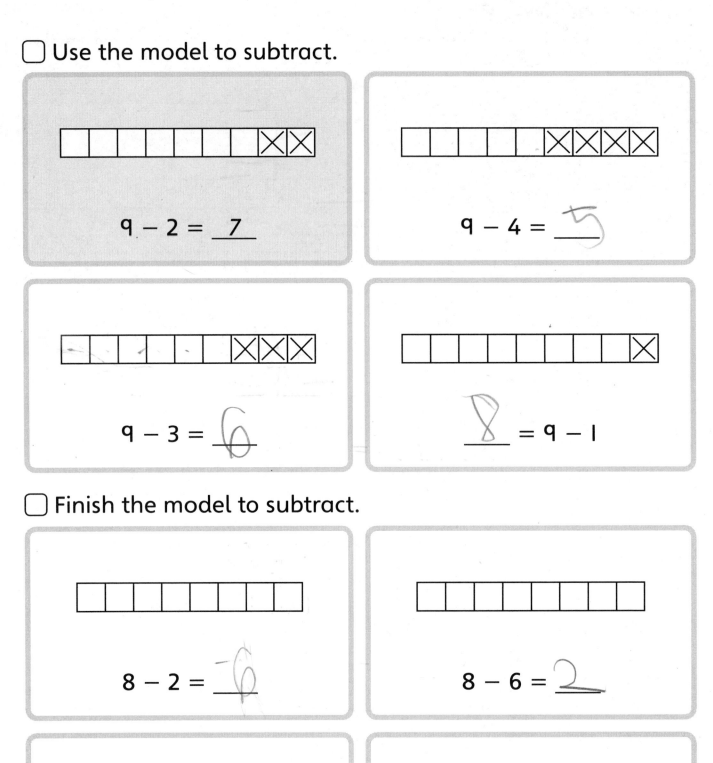

$9 - 2 = \underline{7}$

$9 - 4 = \underline{5}$

$9 - 3 = \underline{6}$

$\underline{8} = 9 - 1$

☐ Finish the model to subtract.

$8 - 2 = \underline{6}$

$8 - 6 = \underline{2}$

$\underline{4} = 8 - 4$

$\underline{3} = 8 - 5$

☐ Write one sentence for both.

2 + 5
4 + 3

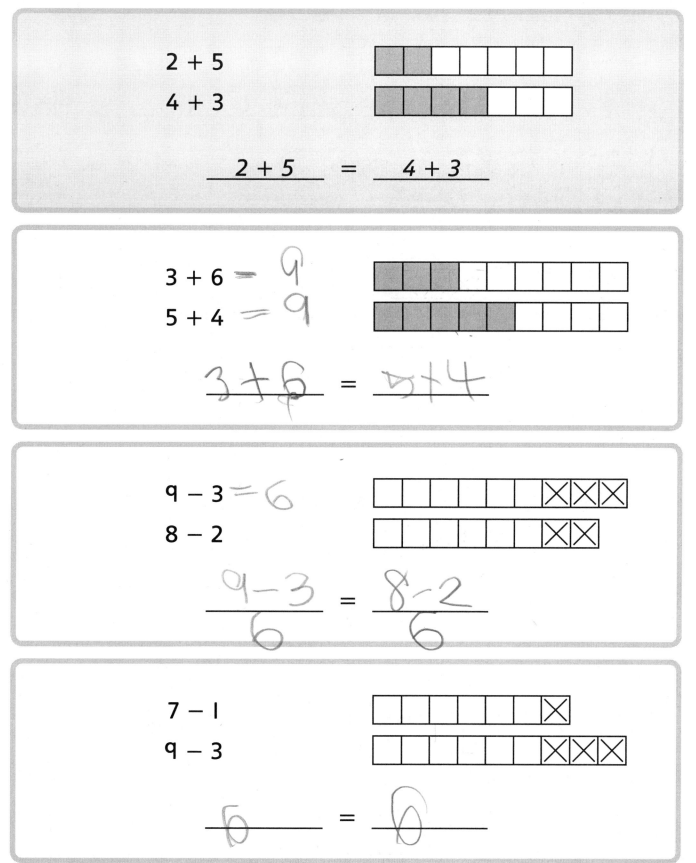

__2 + 5__ = __4 + 3__

3 + 6 = 9
5 + 4 = 9

__3 + 6__ = __5 + 4__

9 − 3 = 6
8 − 2

__9 − 3__ = __8 − 2__
     6          6

7 − 1
9 − 3

__6__ = __6__

☐ Write **equal** or **not equal**.

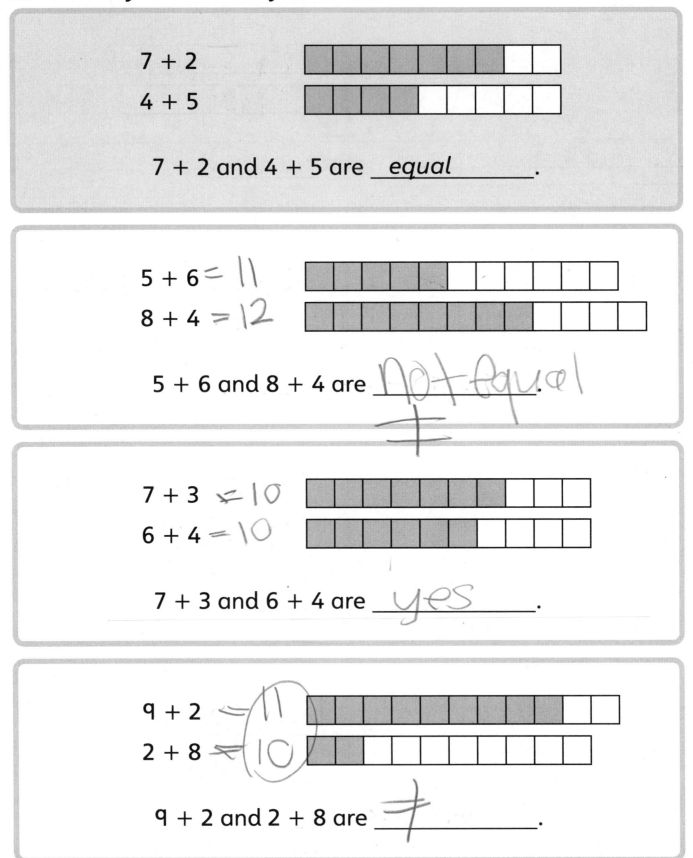

7 + 2

4 + 5

7 + 2 and 4 + 5 are ___equal___ .

5 + 6 = 11

8 + 4 = 12

5 + 6 and 8 + 4 are ___not equal___ .
≠

7 + 3 = 10

6 + 4 = 10

7 + 3 and 6 + 4 are ___yes___ .

9 + 2 = 11

2 + 8 = 10

9 + 2 and 2 + 8 are ___≠___ .

Write equal or not equal.

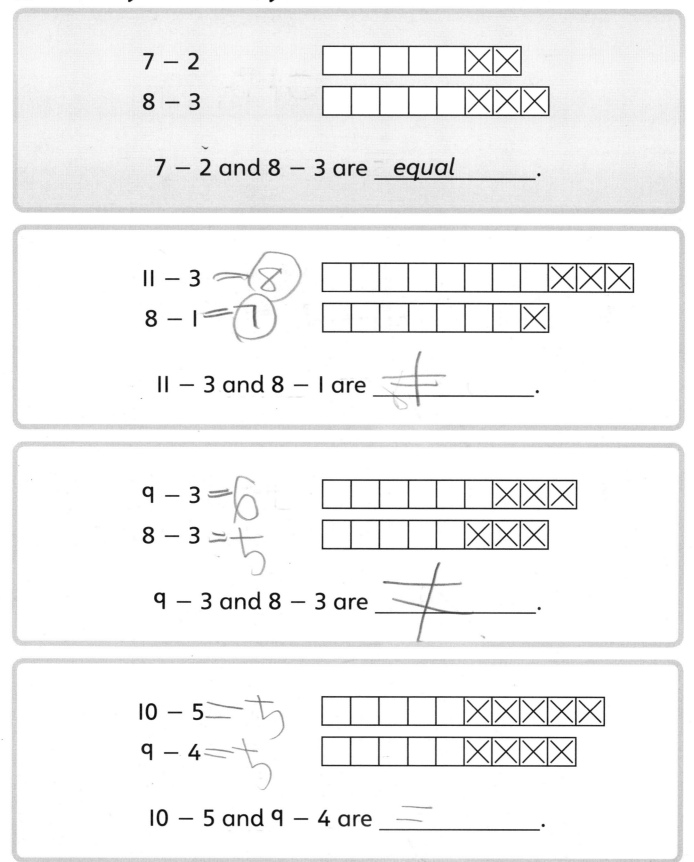

7 − 2

8 − 3

7 − 2 and 8 − 3 are _____equal_____.

11 − 3  8

8 − 1 = 7

11 − 3 and 8 − 1 are ___≠___.

9 − 3 = 6

8 − 3 = 5

9 − 3 and 8 − 3 are ___≠___.

10 − 5 = 5

9 − 4 = 5

10 − 5 and 9 − 4 are ___=___.

○ Write = for equal. Write ≠ for not equal.

8 − 3 = 5

9 − 2 = 7

8 − 3 [≠] 9 − 2

7 + 4 = 11

6 + 6 = 12

7 + 4 [≠] 6 + 6

7 + 3 = 10

8 + 2 = 10

7 + 3 [=] 8 + 2

**Bonus**

12 − 11 = 1

5 − 4 = 1

12 − 11 [=] 5 − 4

# Equality and Inequality with Balances

☐ Add cubes to one side to balance the pans.

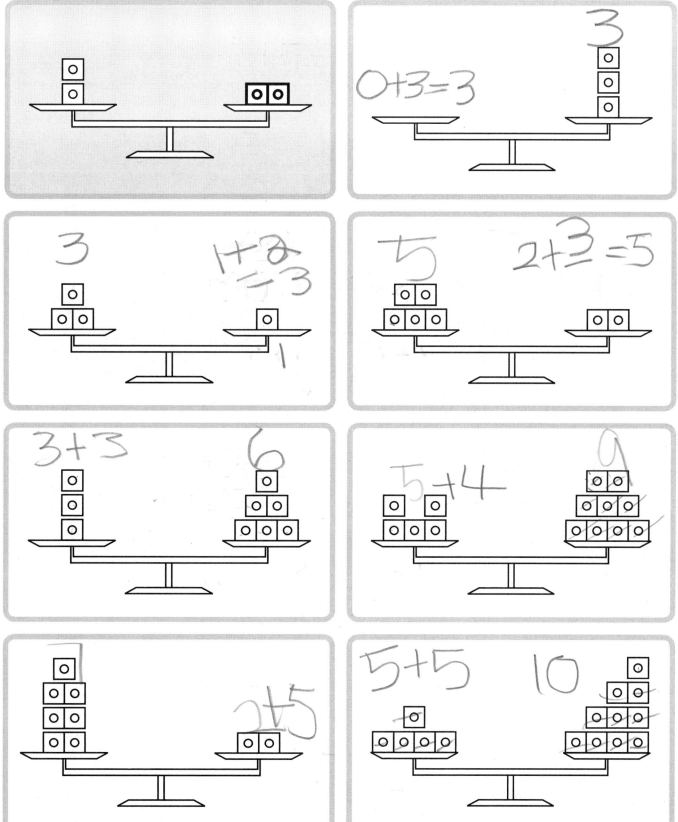

0+3=3

3

1+8
=3
1

5    2+3 =5

3+3    6

5+4    9

2+5

5+5    10

☐ Draw cubes to make the balance correct.

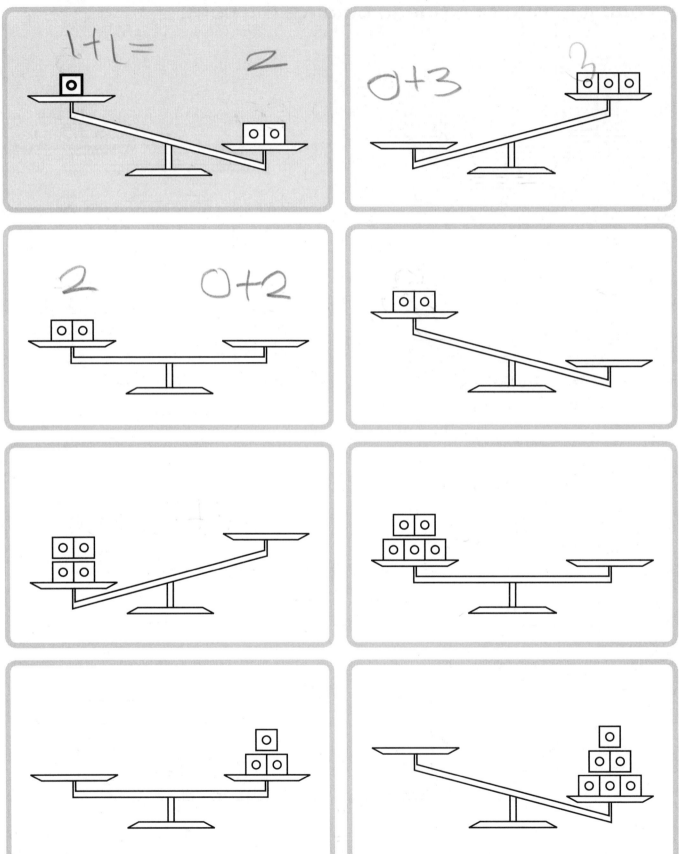

☐ Add balls to one side to balance the pans.
☐ Write an addition sentence.

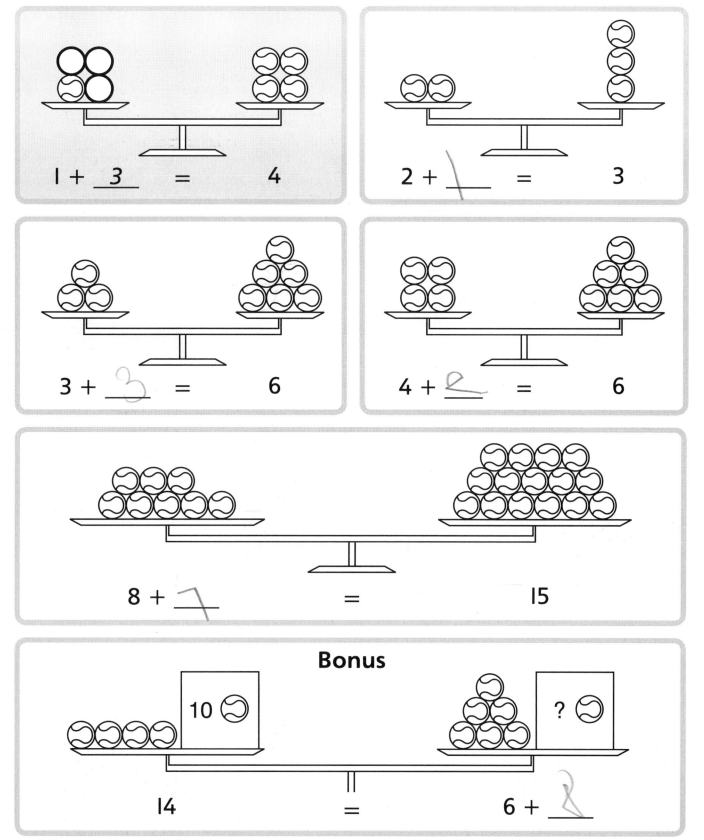

1 + _3_ = 4

2 + _1_ = 3

3 + _3_ = 6

4 + _2_ = 6

8 + _7_ = 15

**Bonus**

14 = 6 + _8_

# Remove cubes from one side to balance the pans.

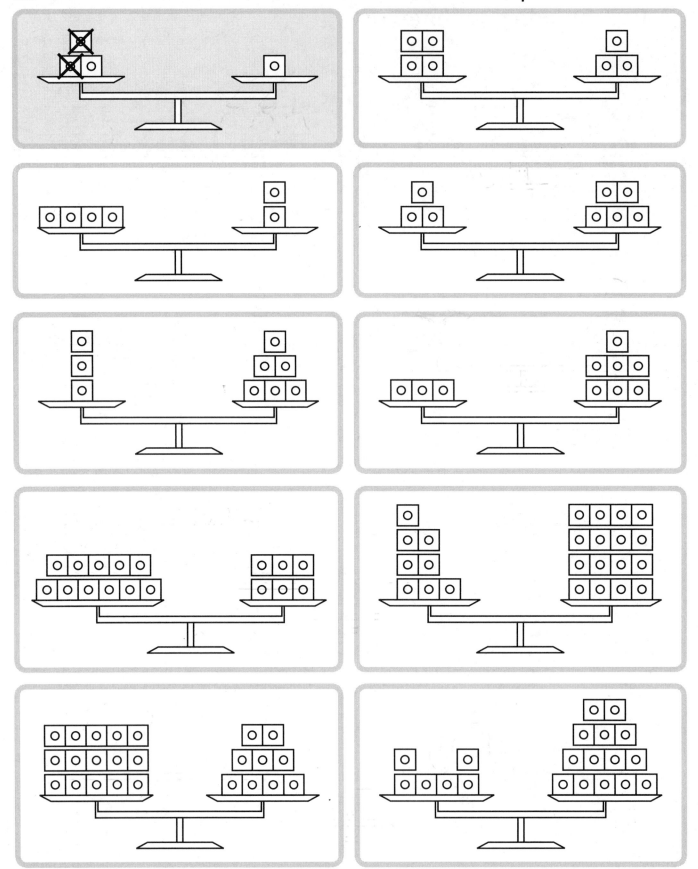

**Number Sense 2-29**

☐ Remove fruits from one side to balance the pans.
☐ Write a subtraction sentence.

6 − __2__ = 4

5 − ___ = 1

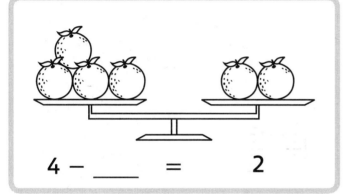

4 − ___ = 2

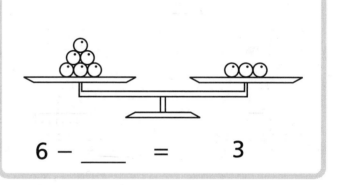

6 − ___ = 3

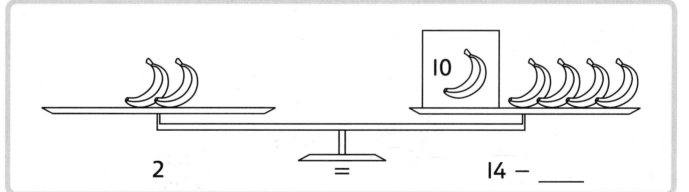

2 = 14 − ___

19 − ___ = 5

# Missing Numbers

☐ Find the missing number.

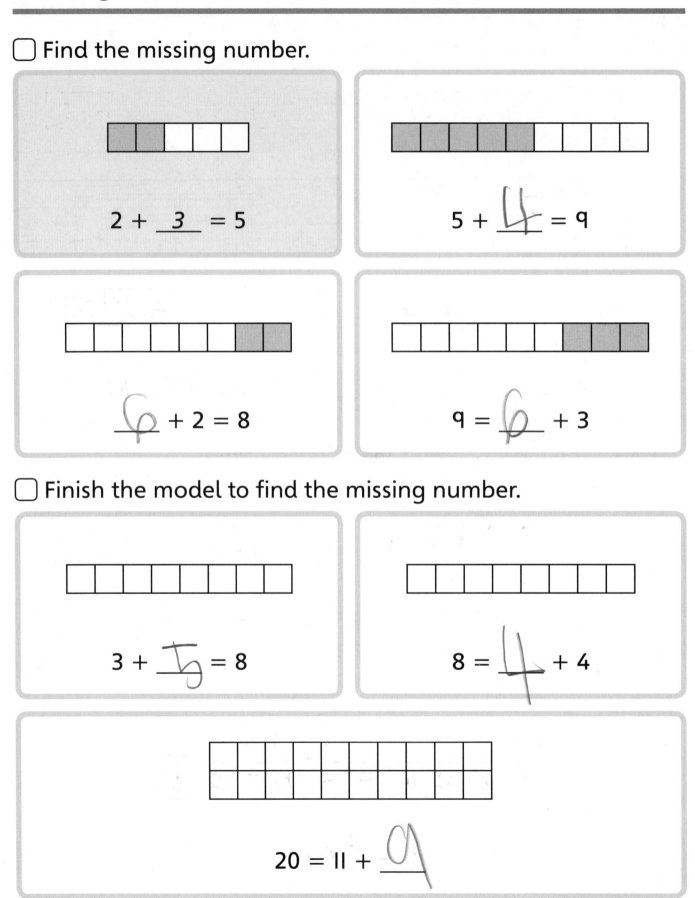

$2 + \underline{\ 3\ } = 5$

$5 + \underline{\ 4\ } = 9$

$\underline{\ 6\ } + 2 = 8$

$9 = \underline{\ 6\ } + 3$

☐ Finish the model to find the missing number.

$3 + \underline{\ 5\ } = 8$

$8 = \underline{\ 4\ } + 4$

$20 = 11 + \underline{\ 9\ }$

⬜ Find the missing number.

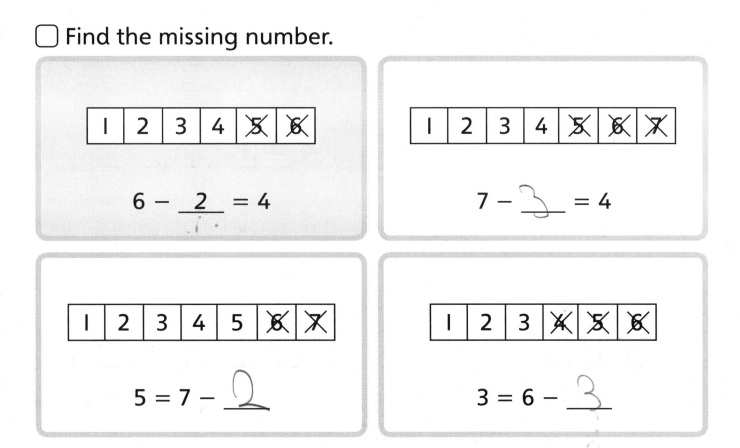

| 1 | 2 | 3 | 4 | ~~5~~ | ~~6~~ |

$6 - \underline{\phantom{2}2\phantom{2}} = 4$

| 1 | 2 | 3 | 4 | ~~5~~ | ~~6~~ | ~~7~~ |

$7 - \underline{\phantom{3}3\phantom{3}} = 4$

| 1 | 2 | 3 | 4 | 5 | ~~6~~ | ~~7~~ |

$5 = 7 - \underline{\phantom{2}2\phantom{2}}$

| 1 | 2 | 3 | ~~4~~ | ~~5~~ | ~~6~~ |

$3 = 6 - \underline{\phantom{3}3\phantom{3}}$

⬜ Finish the model to find the missing number.

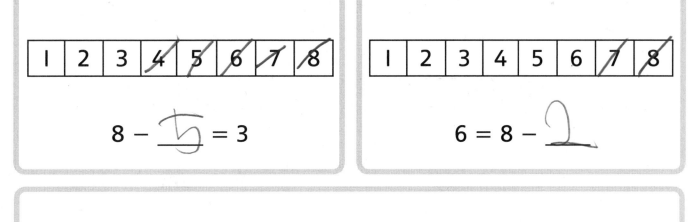

| 1 | 2 | 3 | ~~4~~ | ~~5~~ | ~~6~~ | ~~7~~ | ~~8~~ |

$8 - \underline{\phantom{5}5\phantom{5}} = 3$

| 1 | 2 | 3 | 4 | 5 | 6 | ~~7~~ | ~~8~~ |

$6 = 8 - \underline{\phantom{2}2\phantom{2}}$

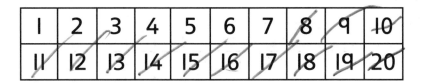

| 1 | 2 | 3 | 4 | 5 | 6 | 7 | ~~8~~ | ~~9~~ | ~~10~~ |
| ~~11~~ | ~~12~~ | ~~13~~ | ~~14~~ | ~~15~~ | ~~16~~ | ~~17~~ | ~~18~~ | ~~19~~ | ~~20~~ |

$20 - \underline{\phantom{13}13\phantom{13}} = 7$

☐ Finish the model to find the missing number.

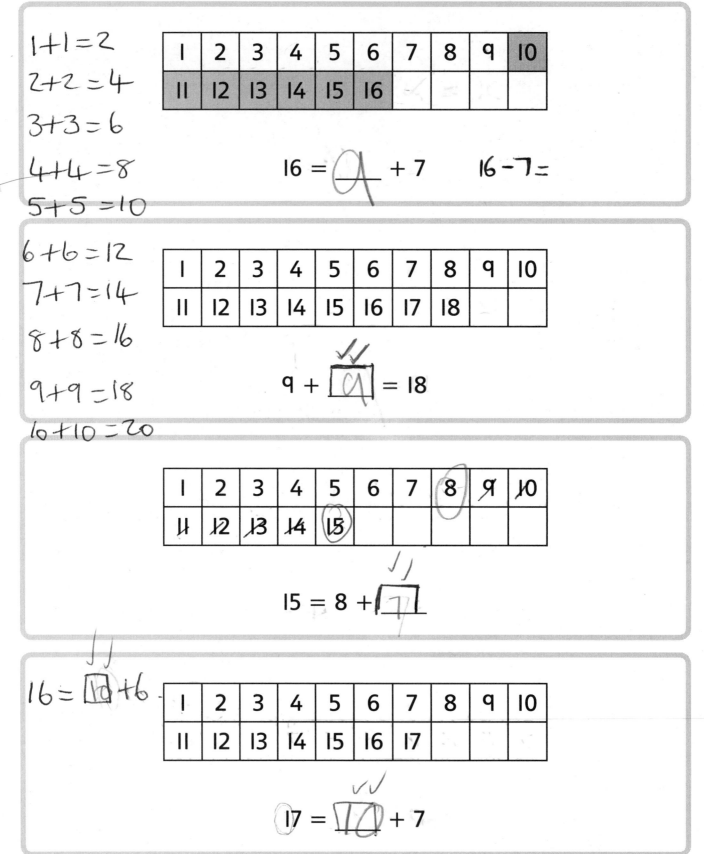

$1+1=2$
$2+2=4$
$3+3=6$
$4+4=8$
$5+5=10$

| 1 | 2 | 3 | 4 | 5 | 6 | 7 | 8 | 9 | 10 |
|---|---|---|---|---|---|---|---|---|----|
| 11 | 12 | 13 | 14 | 15 | 16 | | | | |

$16 = \underline{9} + 7 \qquad 16 - 7 =$

$6+6=12$
$7+7=14$
$8+8=16$
$9+9=18$
$10+10=20$

| 1 | 2 | 3 | 4 | 5 | 6 | 7 | 8 | 9 | 10 |
|---|---|---|---|---|---|---|---|---|----|
| 11 | 12 | 13 | 14 | 15 | 16 | 17 | 18 | | |

$9 + \boxed{9} = 18$

| 1 | 2 | 3 | 4 | 5 | 6 | 7 | 8 | 9 | 10 |
|---|---|---|---|---|---|---|---|---|----|
| 11 | 12 | 13 | 14 | 15 | | | | | |

$15 = 8 + \boxed{7}$

$16 = \boxed{10} + 6$

| 1 | 2 | 3 | 4 | 5 | 6 | 7 | 8 | 9 | 10 |
|---|---|---|---|---|---|---|---|---|----|
| 11 | 12 | 13 | 14 | 15 | 16 | 17 | | | |

$17 = \boxed{10} + 7$

## Finish the model to find the missing number.

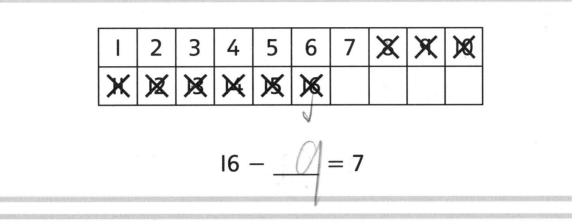

| 1 | 2 | 3 | 4 | 5 | 6 | 7 | X̶ | X̶ | X̶ |
|---|---|---|---|---|---|---|---|---|---|
| X̶ | X̶ | X̶ | X̶ | X̶ | X̶ | | | | |

$$16 - \underline{9} = 7$$

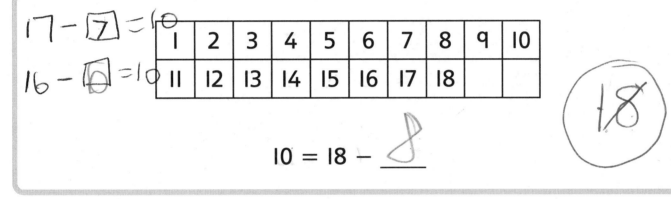

$$17 - \boxed{7} = 10$$
$$16 - \boxed{6} = 10$$

| 1 | 2 | 3 | 4 | 5 | 6 | 7 | 8 | 9 | 10 |
|---|---|---|---|---|---|---|---|---|----|
| 11 | 12 | 13 | 14 | 15 | 16 | 17 | 18 | | |

$$10 = 18 - \underline{8}$$

$\boxed{18}$

| 1 | 2 | 3 | 4 | 5 | 6 | 7 | ⑧ | 9 | 10 |
|---|---|---|---|---|---|---|---|---|----|
| 11 | 12 | 13 | ⑭ | | | | | | |

$$8 = 14 - \underline{6}$$

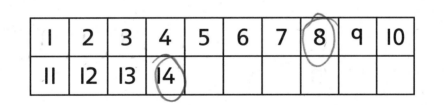

| 1 | 2 | 3 | 4 | 5 | 6 | 7 | 8 | ⑨ | 10 |
|---|---|---|---|---|---|---|---|---|----|
| 11 | 12 | 13 | 14 | 15 | 16 | ⑰ | | | |

$$17 - \boxed{8} = 9$$

Isabella. 8          8-2= 6
Om          2

Henry 5

☐ Finish the model to find the missing number.

George 6

| 1 | 2 | 3 | 4 | 5 | 6 | 7 | ✗ | ✗ | ✗ |
|---|---|---|---|---|---|---|---|---|---|
| ✗ | ✗ | ✗ | ✗ | ✗ | ✗ | ✗ |   |   |   |

8  2  6.

8, 6, 2.

$17 - 10 = 7$

20 + 2 = 22

Bella's age!

22 + 2 = 24

| 1 | 2 | 3 | 4 | 5 | 6 | 7 | 8 | 9 | 10 |
|---|---|---|---|---|---|---|---|---|----|
| 11 | 12 | 13 | 14 | 15 | 16 | 17 | 18 | 19 |   |

$19 = 9 + 10$

$10 + 9 = 19$

| 1 | 2 | 3 | 4 | 5 | 6 | 7 | 8 | 9 | 10 |
|---|---|---|---|---|---|---|---|---|----|
| 11 | 12 | 13 |   |   |   |   |   |   |    |

$7 + 6 = 13$

18 + 6 = 24

24 - 1 = 23.

**Bonus**

| 1 | 2 | 3 | 4 | 5 | 6 | 7 | 8 | 9 | 10 |
|---|---|---|---|---|---|---|---|---|----|
| 11 | 12 | 13 | 14 | 15 | 16 | 17 | 18 | 19 | 20 |

$2 = 19 - 17$

156

# Comparing Number Sentences

$10 + 0 = 10$   $6 + 4 = 10$
$9 + 1 = 10.$   $5 + 5 = 10$

$8 + 2 = 10$
$7 + 3 = 10$

☐ Write two subtraction sentences.
☐ Circle the totals.

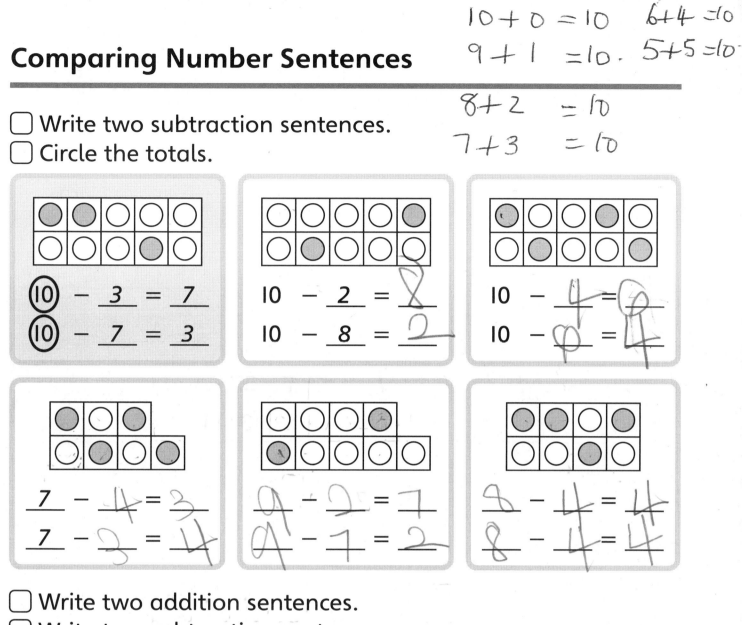

⑩ − _3_ = _7_

⑩ − _7_ = _3_

$10$ − _2_ = 8

$10$ − _8_ = 2

$10$ − 4 = 6

$10$ − 0 = 4

_7_ − 4 = 3

_7_ − 3 = 4

9 − 2 = 7

9 − 7 = 2

8 − 4 = 4

8 − 4 = 4

☐ Write two addition sentences.
☐ Write two subtraction sentences.
☐ Circle the totals.

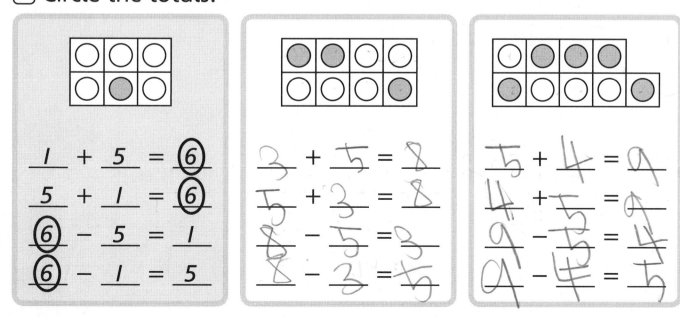

_1_ + _5_ = ⑥

_5_ + _1_ = ⑥

⑥ − _5_ = _1_

⑥ − _1_ = _5_

3 + 5 = 8

5 + 3 = 8

8 − 5 = 3

8 − 3 = 5

5 + 4 = 9

4 + 5 = 9

9 − 4 = 5

9 − 4 = 5

☐ Circle the total.
☐ Write two subtraction sentences for the addition.

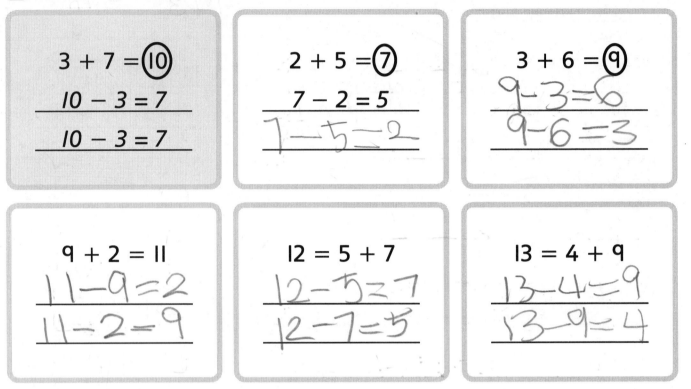

3 + 7 = ⑩

10 − 3 = 7

10 − 3 = 7

2 + 5 = ⑦

7 − 2 = 5

7 − 5 = 2

3 + 6 = ⑨

9 − 3 = 6

9 − 6 = 3

9 + 2 = 11

11 − 9 = 2

11 − 2 = 9

12 = 5 + 7

12 − 5 = 7

12 − 7 = 5

13 = 4 + 9

13 − 4 = 9

13 − 9 = 4

☐ Circle the total.
☐ Write two addition sentences for the subtraction.

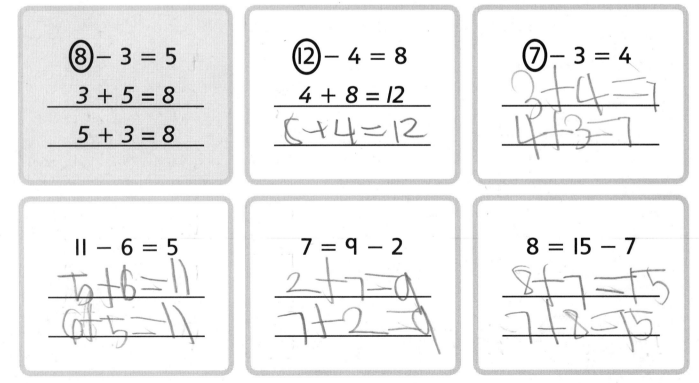

⑧ − 3 = 5

3 + 5 = 8

5 + 3 = 8

⑫ − 4 = 8

4 + 8 = 12

8 + 4 = 12

⑦ − 3 = 4

3 + 4 = 7

4 + 3 = 7

11 − 6 = 5

5 + 6 = 11

6 + 5 = 11

7 = 9 − 2

2 + 7 = 9

7 + 2 = 9

8 = 15 − 7

8 + 7 = 15

7 + 8 = 15

Write four number sentences for each picture.

$4 + 3 = 7$    $3 + 4 = 7$

□ □ □ □ ■ ■ ■

$7 - 3 = 4$    $7 - 4 = 3$

---

$2+6=8$   $6+2=8$

■ ■ □ □ □ □ □ □

$8-2=6$   $8-6=2$

---

$3+2=5$   $2+3=5$

□ □ □ ■ ■

$5-3=2$   $5-2=3$

---

$1+4=5$   $4+1=5$

■ □ □ □ □

$5-4=1$   $5-1=4$

---

$\begin{array}{r} 2 \\ +\ 4 \\ \hline 6 \end{array}$    $\begin{array}{r} 4 \\ +\ 2 \\ \hline 6 \end{array}$

$\begin{array}{r} 6 \\ -\ 4 \\ \hline 2 \end{array}$    $\begin{array}{r} 6 \\ -\ 2 \\ \hline 4 \end{array}$

---

$\begin{array}{r} 6 \\ +\ 1 \\ \hline 7 \end{array}$    $\begin{array}{r} 1 \\ +\ 6 \\ \hline 7 \end{array}$

$\begin{array}{r} 7 \\ -\ 6 \\ \hline 1 \end{array}$    $\begin{array}{r} 7 \\ -\ 1 \\ \hline 6 \end{array}$

# More and Fewer

☐ Draw ◯ or △ to show which is fewer.

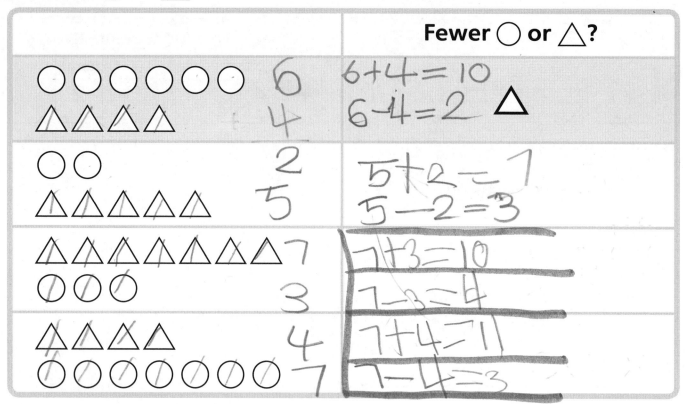

| | Fewer ◯ or △? |
|---|---|
| ◯◯◯◯◯◯ 6 <br> △△△△ 4 | 6+4=10 <br> 6-4=2 △ |
| ◯◯ 2 <br> △△△△△ 5 | 5+2=7 <br> 5-2=3 |
| △△△△△△△ 7 <br> ◯◯◯ 3 | 7+3=10 <br> 7-3=4 |
| △△△△△ 4 <br> ◯◯◯◯◯◯◯ 7 | 7+4=11 <br> 7-4=3 |

☐ Circle **more** or **fewer** △.

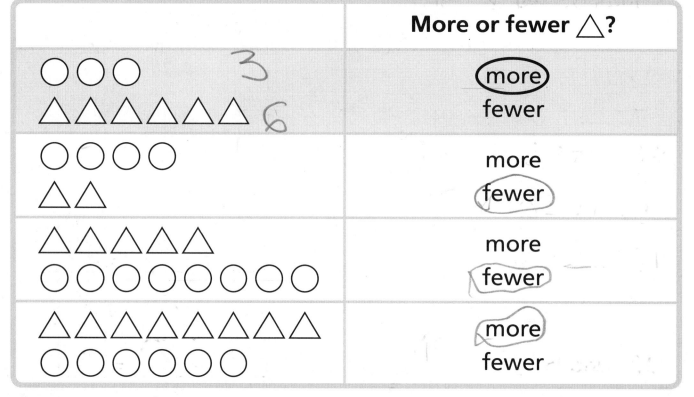

| | More or fewer △? |
|---|---|
| ◯◯◯ 3 <br> △△△△△△ 6 | (more) <br> fewer |
| ◯◯◯◯ <br> △△ | more <br> (fewer) |
| △△△△△ <br> ◯◯◯◯◯◯◯ | more <br> (fewer) |
| △△△△△△△△ <br> ◯◯◯◯◯◯ | (more) <br> fewer |

Draw ◯ or △ to show which is fewer.
Write how many fewer.

| | Fewer ◯ or △? | How many fewer? |
|---|---|---|
| ◯◯◯<br>△△△△△ | ◯ | 2 |
| ◯◯◯◯◯◯<br>△△ | △ | 4 |
| △△△△<br>◯◯◯◯◯◯ | △ | 3 |
| △△△△△△△△△<br>◯◯◯◯ | ◯ | 5 |

Draw ◯ or △ to show which is more.
Find how many more.

| | More ◯ or △? | How many more? |
|---|---|---|
| 5◯ and 8△ | △ | 8 – 5 = 3 |
| 12◯ and 7△ | ◯ | 12 – 7 = 5 |
| 14◯ and 12△ | ◯ | 14 – 12 = 2 |
| 9◯ and 12△ | △ | 12 – 9 = 3 |
| 11◯ and 6△ | ◯ | 11 – 6 = 5 |
| 10◯ and 15△ | △ | 15 – 10 = 5 |

☐ Underline who has fewer.
☐ Find how many fewer.

| | **How many fewer?** |
|---|---|
| <u>Tess</u> has 5 shells.<br>Jack has 8 shells. | $8 - 5 = 3$ |
| Emma has 17 shells.<br><u>Fred</u> has 7 shells. | $17 - 7 = 10$ |
| Ray has 14 shells.<br>Grace has 18 shells. | $18 - 14 = 4$ |
| Ava has 9 shells.<br>Ken has 15 shells. | $15 - 9 = 6$ |
| Nina has 11 shells.<br>Ivan has 4 shells. | $11 - 4 = 7$ |

☐ Find how many more or fewer.

Yu has 8 raisins. Bill has 12 raisins.

How many more raisins does Bill have? $12 - 8 = 4$

Alex has 13 raisins. Ethan has 2 raisins.

How many fewer raisins does Ethan have? $13 - 2 = 11$

Clara has 13 raisins. Amir has 2 raisins.

How many more raisins does Clara have? $13 - 2 = 11$

# Compare Using Pictures

◻ Circle who has more. Underline who has fewer.
◻ Draw triangles for Kim.

| | | | | | | | | |
|---|---|---|---|---|---|---|---|---|
| **(Kim)** has 3 more △ than <u>Sam</u>. | | | | | | | | |
| Sam | △ | △ | △ | △ | △ | | | |
| Kim | △ | △ | △ | △ | △ | △ | △ | △ |

| | | | | | | | |
|---|---|---|---|---|---|---|---|
| Kim has 3 fewer △ than Sam. | | | | | | | |
| Sam | △ | △ | △ | △ | △ | | 5 |
| Kim | 5 — 3 = 2 | | | | | | |

| | | | | | | | |
|---|---|---|---|---|---|---|---|
| Kim has 1 more △ than Sam. | | | | | | | |
| Sam | △ | △ | △ | △ | △ | | |
| Kim | 5 + 1 = 6 | | | | | | |

| | | | | | | | |
|---|---|---|---|---|---|---|---|
| Kim has 2 more △ than Sam. | | | | | | | |
| Sam | △ | △ | △ | △ | △ | | |
| Kim | 5 + 2 = 7 | | | | | | |

| | | | | | | | |
|---|---|---|---|---|---|---|---|
| Kim has 4 fewer △ than Sam. | | | | | | | |
| Sam | △ | △ | △ | △ | △ | | |
| Kim | 5 — 4 = 1 | | | | | | |

☐ Draw triangles for Tess.
☐ Circle how many triangles Tess has.

Glen has 5 △.     △ △ △ △ △                     (5 + 2)

Tess has 2 more
△ than Glen.      △ △ △ △ △ △ △                  5 − 2

Glen has 3 △.     △ △ △                           3 + 2

Tess has 2 fewer
△ than Glen.                                      3 − 2

Glen has 6 △.     △ △ △ △ △ △                     6 + 3

Tess has 3 more
△ than Glen.                                      6 − 3

Glen has 4 △.     △ △ △ △                         4 + 3

Tess has 3 fewer
△ than Glen.                                      4 − 3

Glen has 7 △.     △ △ △ △ △ △ △                   7 + 1

Tess has 1 fewer
△ than Glen.                                      7 − 1

Number Sense 2-33

# Comparing and Word Problems (I)

☐ Circle which is more. Underline which is fewer.
☐ Find how many circles.

| △ | | How many ○? |
|---|---|---|
| 5 | There are 3 more ○ than △. | 5 + 3 = 8 |
| 6 | There are 3 fewer ○ than △. | 6 – 3 = 3 |
| 4 | There are 2 more ○ than △. | 4 + 2 = 6 |
| 9 | There are 6 fewer ○ than △. | 9 – 6 = 3 |
| 15 | There are 4 fewer ○ than △. | 15 – 4 = 11 |
| 13 | There are 5 fewer ○ than △. | 13 – 5 = 8 |
| 9 | There are 4 more ○ than △. | 9 + 4 = 13 |
| 21 | There are 5 more ○ than △. | 21 + 5 = 26 |
| 27 | There are 3 fewer ○ than △. | 27 – 3 = 24 |
| 39 | There are 6 fewer ○ than △. | 39 – 6 = 33 |

☐ Circle which is more. Underline which is fewer.
☐ Add or subtract.

---

Mona has 25 apples.

She has 8 more pears than apples.

How many pears does Mona have?

$25 + 8 = 33$

---

Marko has 46 red flowers.

He has 7 fewer yellow flowers than red flowers.

How many yellow flowers does Marko have?

$46 - 7 = 39$ yellow flowers

---

Tom has 93 blocks.

He has 6 fewer toy cars than blocks.

How many toy cars does Tom have?

$93 - 6 = 87$ toy cars

---

Lynn drew 28 circles.

She drew 9 more triangles than circles.

How many triangles did Lynn draw?

$28 + 9 = 37$ triangles

---

# Comparing and Word Problems (2)

☐ Underline **more** or **fewer**.

Maria has 3 more stickers than Ben.
Ben has more / <u>fewer</u> stickers than Maria.

Maria has 3 <u>fewer</u> stickers than Ben.
<u>Ben</u> has (more) / fewer stickers than Maria.

Carl has 2 more stickers than Jen.
Jen has more / <u>fewer</u> stickers than Carl.

Carl has 2 fewer stickers than Jen.
Jen has more / fewer stickers than Carl.

☐ Circle who has more. <u>Underline</u> who has fewer.
☐ Draw triangles for Rani.

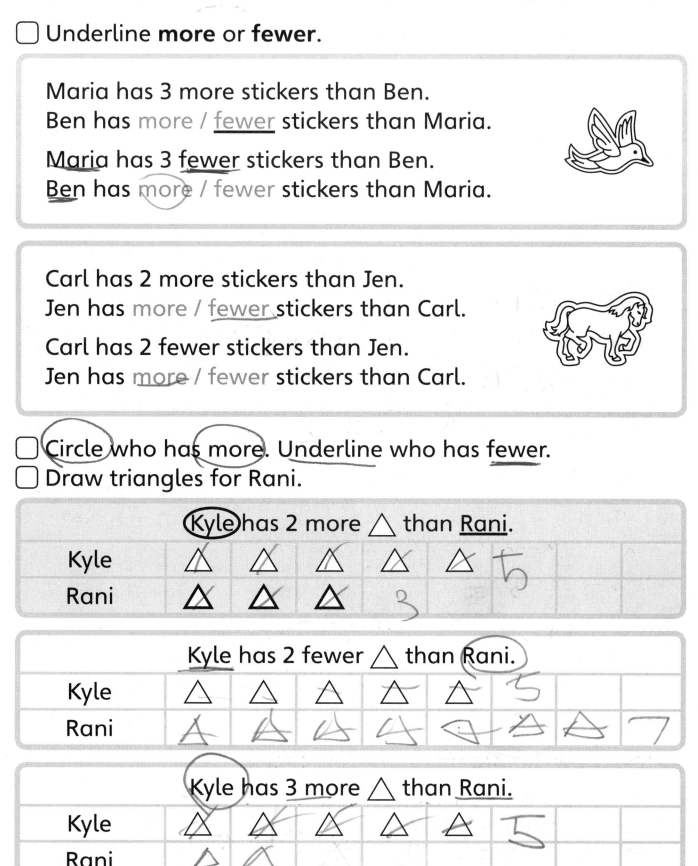

(Kyle) has 2 more △ than <u>Rani</u>.

| Kyle | △ △ △ △ △ 5 |
| Rani | △ △ △ 3 |

Kyle has 2 fewer △ than (Rani.)

| Kyle | △ △ △ △ △ 5 |
| Rani | △ △ △ △ △ △ △ 7 |

Kyle has 3 more △ than <u>Rani</u>.

| Kyle | △ △ △ △ △ 5 |
| Rani | △ △ |

Liz has 10 grapes.

☐ Circle who has more grapes. Underline who has fewer grapes.
☐ Fill in the table.

| | Does Jon have more or fewer? | How many does Jon have? |
|---|---|---|
| (Liz) has 2 more grapes than <u>Jon</u>. | *fewer* | 10 (−) 2 |
| <u>Liz</u> has 2 fewer grapes than (Jon). | more | 10 (+) 2 |
| (Liz) has 3 more grapes than <u>Jon</u>. | fewer | 10 (−) 3 |
| <u>Liz</u> has 3 fewer grapes than (Jon). | More | 10 (+) 3 |

☐ Circle who has more. Underline who has fewer.
☐ Fill in the table.

| | Does Don have more or fewer? | How many does Don have? |
|---|---|---|
| <u>Amy</u> has 8 grapes.<br><u>Amy</u> has 3 fewer grapes than (Don) | *more* | $8 + 3$ = _11_ |
| Amy has 8 grapes.<br>(Amy) has 3 more grapes than <u>Don</u>. | fewer | $8 - 3 = 5$ |
| Amy has 6 grapes.<br><u>Amy</u> has 5 fewer grapes than (Don). | More | $6 + 5$ = _11_ |
| Amy has 11 grapes.<br>(Amy) has 7 more grapes than <u>Don</u>. | fewer | $11 - 7$ = _4_ |

☐ Circle who has more pencils. Underline who has fewer pencils.
☐ Find how many pencils David has.

Hanna has 26 pencils.

Hanna has 3 fewer pencils than (David)

How many pencils does David have?     26 + 3 = 29

Hanna has 43 pencils.

(Hanna) has 10 more pencils than David.

How many pencils does David have?     43 − 10 = 33

Hanna has 26 pencils.

Hanna has 7 fewer pencils than David.

How many pencils does David have?     26 + 7 = 33

Hanna has 65 pencils.

Hanna has 8 more pencils than David.

How many pencils does David have?     65 − 8 = 57

Hanna has 79 pencils.

Hanna has 9 more pencils than David.

How many pencils does David have?     79 − 9 = 70

# Subtracting in Word Problems

☐ Subtract by counting forwards.
☐ Write a sentence to describe how many **more**.

Sara has 12 marbles.
Ray has 8 marbles.

_____Sara has 4 more marbles than Ray._____

Sara has 7 apples.
Sara has 9 oranges.

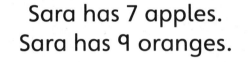
9 − 7 = 2

Ray has 8 crayons.
Ray has 5 markers.

8 − 5 = 3

Sara has 6 crayons.
Ray has 10 crayons.

10 − 6 = 4

☐ Circle the correct way to answer the question.
☐ Write the answer.

Kate had five bananas.
She ate three bananas.

$5 + 3$　　（$5 - 3$）

How many bananas are **left**? __2__

---

There are eight big pencils.
There are five little pencils.

（$8 + 5$）　　$8 - 5$

How many pencils **altogether**? __13__

---

There are eight big pencils.
There are five little pencils.

$8 + 5$　　（$8 - 5$）

How many **more** big pencils **than** little pencils? __3__

---

There are fourteen red balloons.
There are three blue balloons.

$14 + 3$　　（$14 - 3$）

How many **more** red balloons **than** blue balloons? __11__

---

There are fourteen red balloons.
There are three blue balloons.

（$14 + 3$）　　$14 - 3$

How many balloons **in total**? __17__

---

Cathy has eleven crayons.
Seven of them are red.

$11 + 7$　　（$11 - 7$）

How many are **not** red? __4__

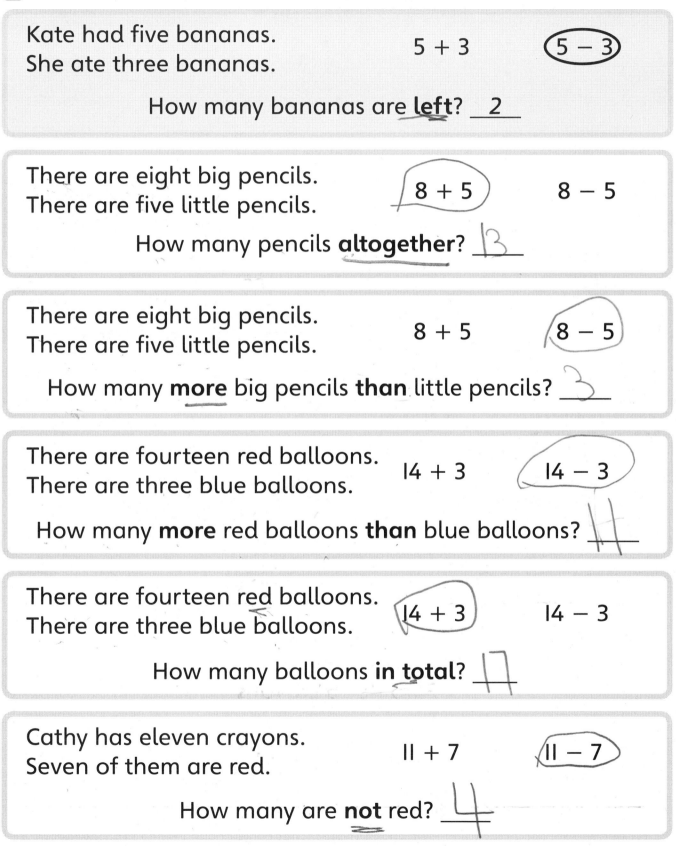

# More Missing Numbers

☐ Find the missing number by adding.

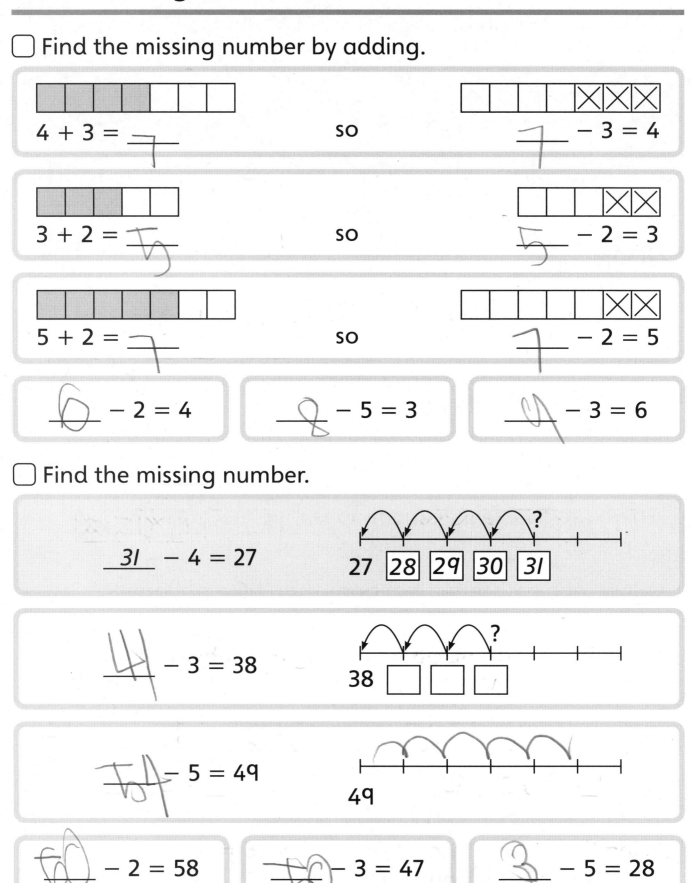

4 + 3 = 7                    so                    7 − 3 = 4

3 + 2 = 5                    so                    5 − 2 = 3

5 + 2 = 7                    so                    7 − 2 = 5

6 − 2 = 4          8 − 5 = 3          9 − 3 = 6

☐ Find the missing number.

31 − 4 = 27

27  [28] [29] [30] [31]

4 − 3 = 38

38 ☐ ☐ ☐

54 − 5 = 49

49

60 − 2 = 58          50 − 3 = 47          3 − 5 = 28

⬜ Find the missing number by counting forwards.

27 + 4 = __31__

so

__31__ − 4 = 27

36 + 3 = _39_

so

_39_ − 3 = 36

2 + 25 = _27_

so

_27_ − 25 = 2

_19_ − 13 = 6

_26_ − 5 = 21

_41_ − 4 = 37

⬜ Find the missing number by using a picture.

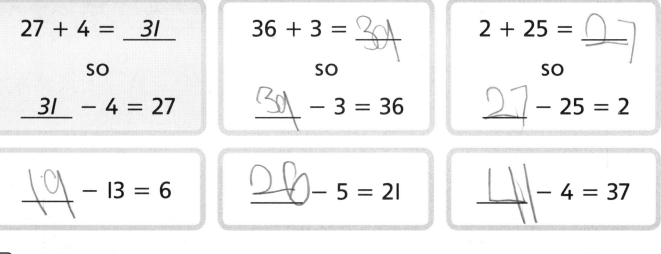

| 1 | 2 | 3 | 4 | 5 | 6̶ | 7̶ | 8̶ | 9̶ |

__9__ − 4 = 5

| 1 | 2 | 3 | 4 | 5 | 6 | 7̶ | 8̶ |

_8_ − 2 = 6

| 1 | 2 | 3 | 4 | 5̶ | 6̶ | 7̶ |

_7_ − 3 = 4

| 1 | 2 | 3̶ | 4̶ | 5̶ | 6̶ |

6 − _4_ = 2

⬜ Find the missing number by using a number line.

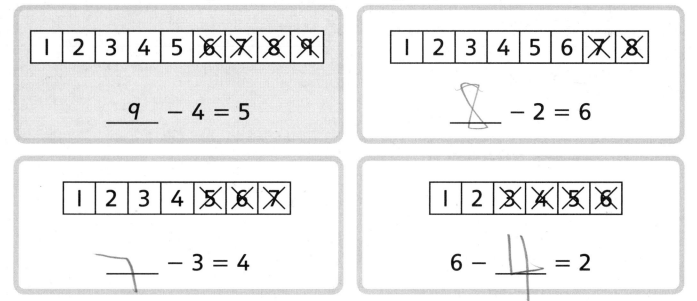

```
 ├──┼──┼──┼──┼──┼──┤
25  26  27  28  29  30  31
```

_28_ − 3 = 25

```
 ├──┼──┼──┼──┼──┼──┤
25  26  27  28  29  30  31
```

_31_ − 5 = 26

📝 Find the missing number in _31_ − 26 = 5.
Explain how you found it.

# Missing Numbers in Word Problems

☑ Write the number sentence for the story.

There are ■ red marbles.
There are 5 blue marbles.
There are 9 marbles altogether.

$$\begin{array}{r} \blacksquare \\ + \quad 5 \\ \hline 9 \end{array}$$

There are 7 red marbles.
There are 3 blue marbles.
There are ■ marbles altogether.

$7 + 3 = 10$

There are 4 red marbles.
There are ■ blue marbles.
There are 6 marbles altogether.

$6 - 4 = 2$

There are 5 red marbles.
There are ■ blue marbles.
There are 8 marbles altogether.

$8 - 5 = 3$

There are ■ red marbles.
There are 2 blue marbles.
There are 7 marbles altogether.

$7 - 2 = 5$

Write the number sentence for the story.

There are ☐ children at the park.

There are 3 adults at the park.

There are 8 people altogether.

$$+\ \frac{3}{8}$$

---

There are 3 glasses of milk.

There are 8 glasses of juice.

There are ☐ glasses altogether.

$8 + 3 = 9$

---

Luc has 4 stickers.

Tristan has ☐ stickers.

Together, they have 9 stickers.

$9 - 4 = 5$

---

Tasha has ☐ hockey cards.

Tasha has 2 baseball cards.

Tasha has 7 cards altogether.

$7 - 2 = 5$

---

4 children were playing soccer.

3 more joined them.

Then there were ☐ children playing.

$4 + 3 = 7$

Fill in the missing numbers.

☐ Write the number sentence for the story.

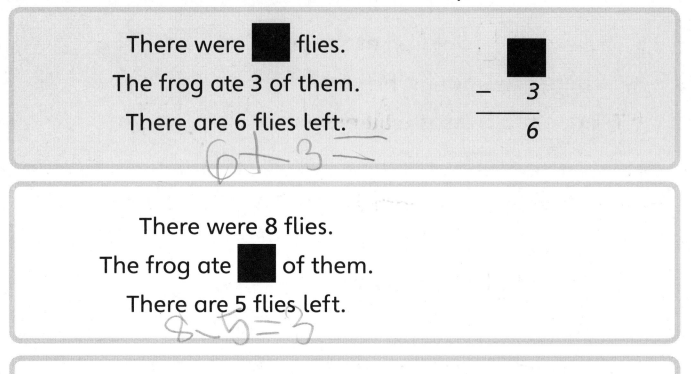

There were ■ flies.
The frog ate 3 of them.
There are 6 flies left.

$$-\ \frac{3}{6}$$

6+3=

There were 8 flies.
The frog ate ■ of them.
There are 5 flies left.

8-5=3

There were 7 flies.
The frog ate 4 of them.
There are ■ flies left.

7-4=3

There were 9 flies.
The frog ate ■ of them.
There are 4 flies left.

9-4=5

There were ■ flies.
The frog ate 2 of them.
There are 5 flies left.

2+5=7

☐ Write the number sentence for the story.

There were ☐ children playing.

3 of them went home.

There are 5 children still playing.

$\boxed{8}$
$-\ \ 3$
$\overline{\phantom{xx}5}$

$5+3=8$

---

There are 7 marbles.

4 of them are red.

☐ marbles are not red.

$7=4=3$

---

Jayden has 8 cousins.

☐ cousins live outside of Canada.

3 cousins live in Canada.

$8-3=5$

---

Jayden has 8 cousins.

3 cousins live in Canada.

☐ cousins live outside of Canada.

$8-3=5$

---

Luc had ☐ stickers.

He gave 2 away.

He has 6 left.

$6+2=8$

---

☐ Fill in the missing numbers.

**Number Sense 2-38**

☐ Match the number sentence to the story.
☐ Fill in the missing number.

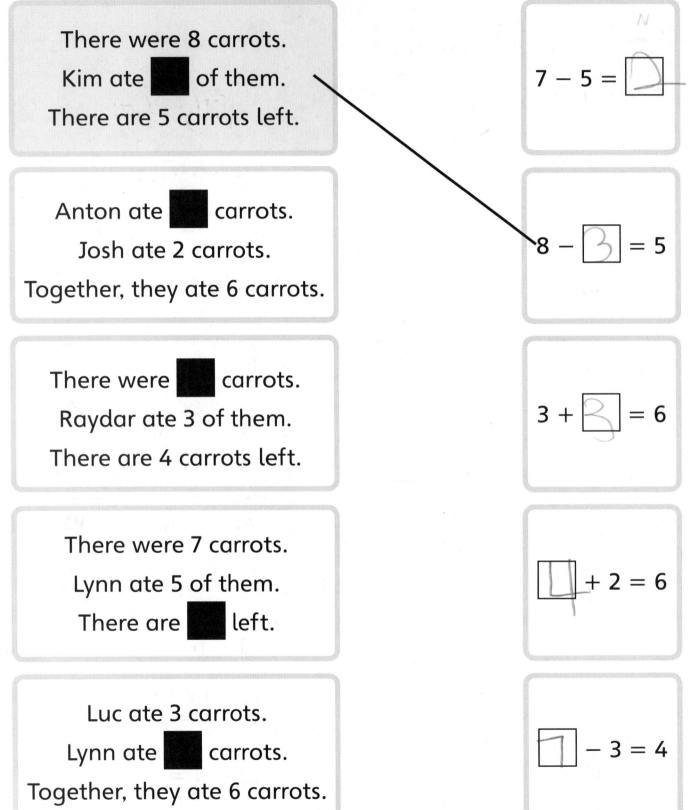

There were 8 carrots.
Kim ate ▮ of them.
There are 5 carrots left.

$7 - 5 = \boxed{2}$

Anton ate ▮ carrots.
Josh ate 2 carrots.
Together, they ate 6 carrots.

$8 - \boxed{3} = 5$

There were ▮ carrots.
Raydar ate 3 of them.
There are 4 carrots left.

$3 + \boxed{3} = 6$

There were 7 carrots.
Lynn ate 5 of them.
There are ▮ left.

$\boxed{4} + 2 = 6$

Luc ate 3 carrots.
Lynn ate ▮ carrots.
Together, they ate 6 carrots.

$\boxed{7} - 3 = 4$

# Making 10

☐ Hold up the correct number of fingers.

How many fingers are not up?

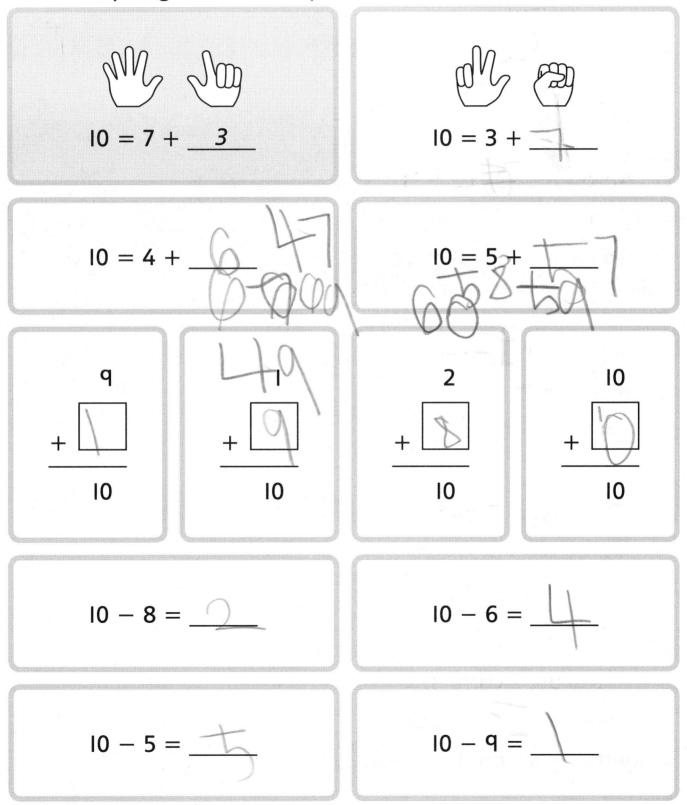

$10 = 7 + \underline{\quad 3 \quad}$

$10 = 3 + \underline{\quad 7 \quad}$

$10 = 4 + \underline{\quad 6 \quad}$

$10 = 5 + \underline{\quad 5 \quad}$

$$
\begin{array}{r}
9 \\
+\ \boxed{1} \\
\hline
10
\end{array}
$$

$$
\begin{array}{r}
1 \\
+\ \boxed{9} \\
\hline
10
\end{array}
$$

$$
\begin{array}{r}
2 \\
+\ \boxed{8} \\
\hline
10
\end{array}
$$

$$
\begin{array}{r}
10 \\
+\ \boxed{0} \\
\hline
10
\end{array}
$$

$10 - 8 = \underline{\quad 2 \quad}$

$10 - 6 = \underline{\quad 4 \quad}$

$10 - 5 = \underline{\quad 5 \quad}$

$10 - 9 = \underline{\quad 1 \quad}$

☐ Circle the number that makes 10 with the number in the box.

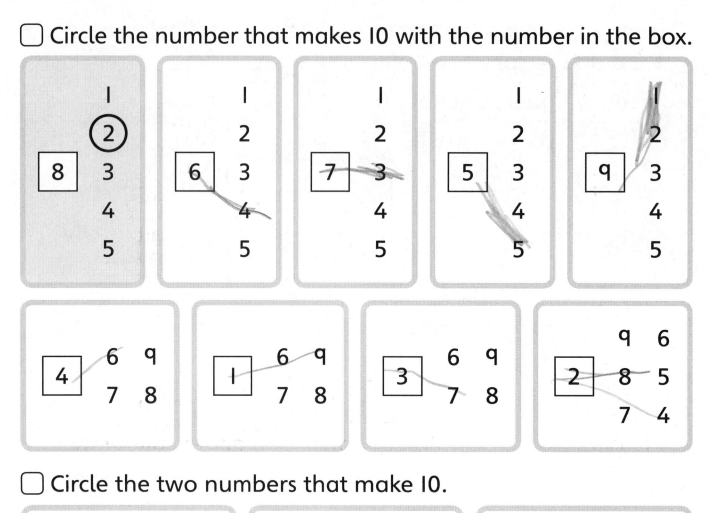

☐ Circle the two numbers that make 10.

| 4 | 5 | 6 |
|---|---|---|

| 3 | 7 | 9 |
|---|---|---|

| 4 | 5 | 5 |
|---|---|---|

| 1 | 2 | 3 | 9 |
|---|---|---|---|

| 4 | 5 | 6 | 7 |
|---|---|---|---|

| 2 | 4 | 6 | 9 |
|---|---|---|---|

| 1 | 9 | 3 | 5 |
|---|---|---|---|

| 2 | 4 | 3 | 8 |
|---|---|---|---|

| 2 | 3 | 7 | 9 |
|---|---|---|---|

| 1 | 2 | 6 | 7 | 8 |
|---|---|---|---|---|

| 2 | 3 | 4 | 7 | 9 |
|---|---|---|---|---|

| 1 | 3 | 4 | 8 | 9 |
|---|---|---|---|---|

| 2 | 3 | 6 | 8 | 9 |
|---|---|---|---|---|

| 2 | 3 | 4 | 5 | 6 |
|---|---|---|---|---|

| 3 | 5 | 6 | 7 | 8 |
|---|---|---|---|---|

☐ Write the missing numbers.

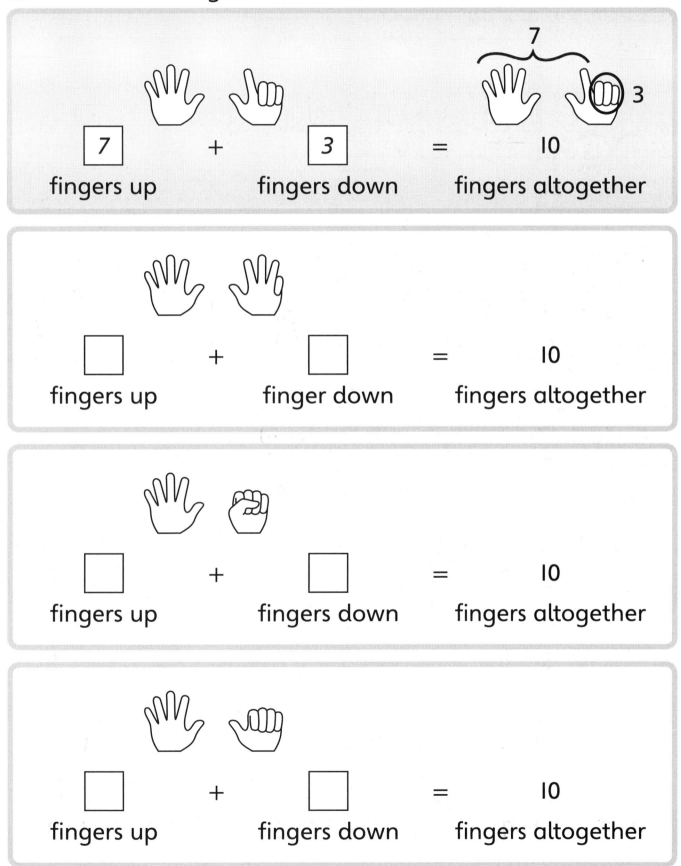

7
fingers up

+

3
fingers down

=

7

10
fingers altogether

3

☐
fingers up

+

☐
finger down

=

10
fingers altogether

☐
fingers up

+

☐
fingers down

=

10
fingers altogether

☐
fingers up

+

☐
fingers down

=

10
fingers altogether

# Adding 10 and Subtracting 10

☐ Circle the next 10 numbers.
☐ Add 10.

| 1 | 2 | 3 | **4** | ⑤ | ⑥ | ⑦ | ⑧ | ⑨ | ⑩ |
|---|---|---|---|---|---|---|---|---|---|
| ⑪ | ⑫ | ⑬ | ⑭ | 15 | 16 | 17 | 18 | 19 | 20 |

$4 + 10 = 14$

| 11 | 12 | 13 | 14 | 15 | 16 | 17 | 18 | **19** | 20 |
|---|---|---|---|---|---|---|---|---|---|
| 21 | 22 | 23 | 24 | 25 | 26 | 27 | 28 | 29 | 30 |

$19 + 10 = 29$

| 31 | 32 | 33 | 34 | 35 | 36 | 37 | **38** | 39 | 40 |
|---|---|---|---|---|---|---|---|---|---|
| 41 | 42 | 43 | 44 | 45 | 46 | 47 | 48 | 49 | 50 |

$38 + 10 = 40$

| 81 | 82 | 83 | 84 | 85 | 86 | 87 | 88 | 89 | **90** |
|---|---|---|---|---|---|---|---|---|---|
| 91 | 92 | 93 | 94 | 95 | 96 | 97 | 98 | 99 | 100 |

$90 + 10 = 100$

☐ Add 10 by moving down a row.

| 1 | 2 | **3** | 4 | 5 | 6 | **7** | 8 | **9** | 10 |
|---|---|---|---|---|---|---|---|---|---|
| 11 | 12 | 13 | 14 | 15 | 16 | 17 | 18 | 19 | 20 |

$3 + 10 = 13$
$7 + 10 = 17$
$9 + 10 = 19$

☐ Move down a row to add 10.

| 1 | 2 | 3 | 4 | 5 | 6 | 7 | 8 | 9 | 10 |
|---|---|---|---|---|---|---|---|---|---|
| 11 | 12 | 13 | 14 | 15 | 16 | 17 | 18 | 19 | 20 |
| 21 | 22 | 23 | 24 | 25 | 26 | 27 | 28 | 29 | 30 |
| 31 | 32 | 33 | 34 | 35 | 36 | 37 | 38 | 39 | 40 |

$2 + 10 = \underline{12}$    $8 + 10 = \underline{18}$    $20 + 10 = \underline{30}$

$17 + 10 = \underline{37}$    $25 + 10 = \underline{35}$    $19 + 10 = \underline{20}$

$11 + 10 = \underline{21}$    $23 + 10 = \underline{33}$    $30 + 10 = \underline{400}$

What comes out of the adding 10 machine?

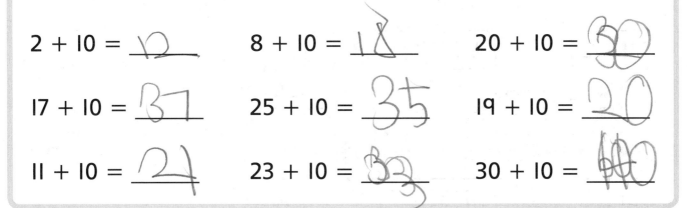

+ 10    26 → 36    + 10    13 → ☐    + 10    12 → ☐    + 10    29 → 30

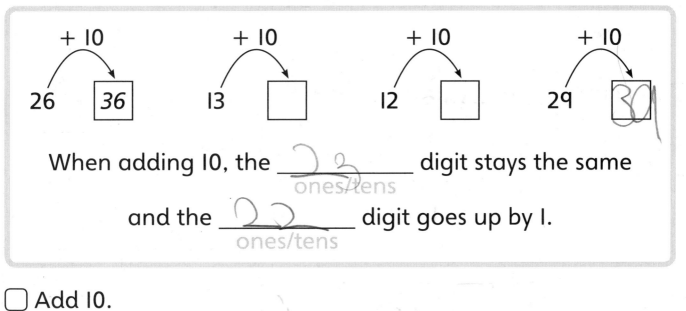

When adding 10, the _____ 23 _____ digit stays the same
ones/tens

and the _____ 22 _____ digit goes up by 1.
ones/tens

☐ Add 10.

$64 + 10 = \underline{74}$    $55 + 10 = \underline{65}$    $87 + 10 = \underline{97}$

☐ Circle the previous 10 numbers.
☐ Subtract 10.

| 1 | 2 | 3 | 4 | 5 | 6 | ⑦ | ⑧ | ⑨ | ⑩ |
|---|---|---|---|---|---|---|---|---|---|
| ⑪ | ⑫ | ⑬ | ⑭ | ⑮ | ⑯ | 17 | 18 | 19 | 20 |

$17 - 10 = \underline{7}$

| 11 | 12 | 13 | 14 | 15 | 16 | 17 | 18 | 19 | 20 |
|----|----|----|----|----|----|----|----|----|----|
| 21 | 22 | 23 | 24 | 25 | 26 | 27 | 28 | 29 | 30 |

$30 - 10 = \underline{20}$

| 41 | 42 | 43 | 44 | 45 | 46 | 47 | 48 | 49 | 50 |
|----|----|----|----|----|----|----|----|----|----|
| 51 | 52 | 53 | 54 | 55 | 56 | 57 | 58 | 59 | 60 |

$52 - 10 = \underline{40}$

☐ Move up a row to subtract 10.

| 71 | 72 | 73 | 74 | 75 | 76 | 77 | 78 | 79 | 80 |
|----|----|----|----|----|----|----|----|----|----|
| 81 | 82 | 83 | 84 | 85 | 86 | 87 | 88 | 89 | 90 |

$82 - 10 = \underline{72}$

$85 - 10 = \underline{75}$

$90 - 10 = \underline{80}$

When subtracting 10, the _____ digit stays the same
　　　　　　　　　　　　　ones/tens

and the _____ digit goes _____ by 1.
　　　　　ones/tens　　　　　　　　　　up/down

☐ Subtract 10.

$76 - 10 = \underline{66}$　　$38 - 10 = \underline{28}$　　$99 - 10 = \underline{89}$

☐ Add 10 by adding a tens block.

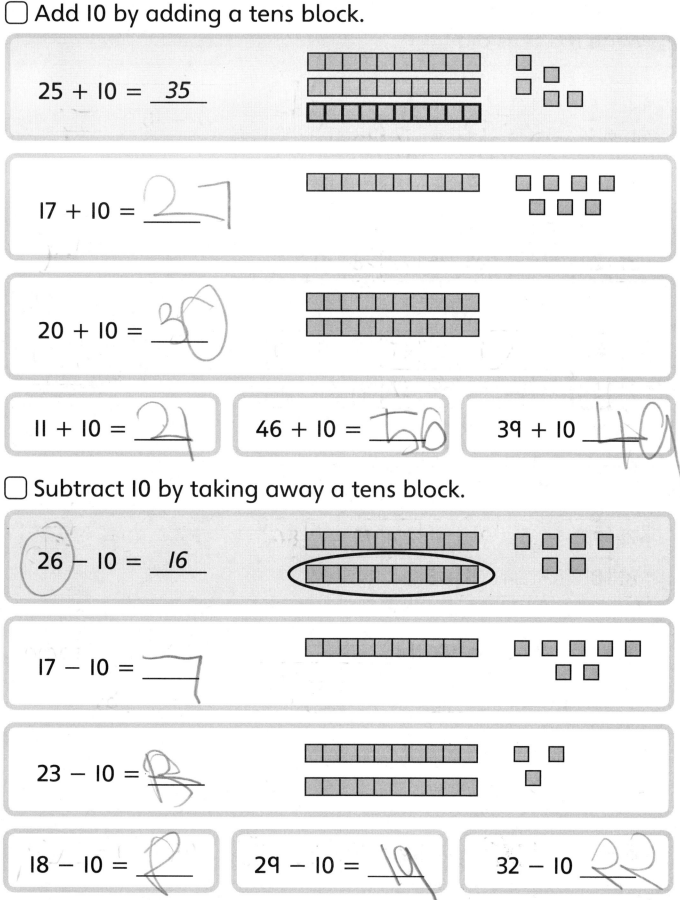

25 + 10 = __35__

17 + 10 = __27__

20 + 10 = __30__

11 + 10 = __21__    46 + 10 = __56__    39 + 10 __49__

☐ Subtract 10 by taking away a tens block.

26 − 10 = __16__

17 − 10 = __7__

23 − 10 = __13__

18 − 10 = __8__    29 − 10 = __19__    32 − 10 __22__

# Adding and Subtracting 10 Mentally

☐ Write the tens digit.

42 + 10 = __5__ 2  37 + 10 = __4__ 7  16 + 10 = __2__ 6

73 + 10 = __8__ 3  56 + 10 = __6__ 6  45 + 10 = __5__ 5

☐ Write the ones digit.

24 + 10 = 3 __4__  62 + 10 = 7 __2__  28 + 10 = 3 __8__

40 + 10 = 5 __0__  66 + 10 = 7 __6__  53 + 10 = 6 __3__

☐ Write the missing digit.

13 + 10 = __2__ 3  87 + 10 = __9__ 7  68 + 10 = __7__ __8__

47 + 10 = __5__ __7__  32 + 10 = __4__ 2  75 + 10 = __8__ __5__

☐ Add 10.

43 + 10 = __5__ __3__  7 + 10 = __10__ __7__  18 + 10 = __10__ __8__

32 + 10 = __42__  25 + 10 = __35__  4 + 10 = __14__

60 + 10 = __70__  55 + 10 = __65__  9 + 10 = __10__

◯ Write the tens digit.

$42 - 10 = \underline{\phantom{8}2}$

$37 - 10 = \underline{2\phantom{7}}7$

$26 - 10 = \underline{1\phantom{6}}6$

$50 - 10 = \underline{4\phantom{0}}0$

$78 - 10 = \underline{6\phantom{8}}8$

$45 - 10 = \underline{3\phantom{5}}5$

◯ Write the ones digit.

$24 - 10 = \underline{1}\ \underline{4}$

$34 - 10 = \underline{2}\ \underline{4}$

$29 - 10 = \underline{1}\ \underline{9}$

$28 - 10 = \underline{1}\ \underline{8}$

$54 - 10 = \underline{4}\ \underline{4}$

$76 - 10 = \underline{6}\ \underline{6}$

◯ Write the missing digit.

$74 - 10 = \underline{6}\ \underline{4}$

$36 - 10 = \underline{2}\ \underline{6}$

$28 - 10 = \underline{1}\ \underline{8}$

$87 - 10 = \underline{7}\ \underline{7}$

$68 - 10 = \underline{5}\ \underline{8}$

$47 - 10 = \underline{3}\ \underline{7}$

◯ Subtract 10.

$41 - 10 = \underline{3}\ \underline{1}$

$17 - 10 = \underline{7}\ \underline{7}$

$38 - 10 = \underline{2}\ \underline{8}$

$18 - 10 = \underline{8}\ \underline{\phantom{0}}$

$80 - 10 = \underline{7}\ \underline{0}$

$16 - 10 = \underline{6}\ \underline{\phantom{0}}$

$54 - 10 = \underline{4}\ \underline{4}$

$31 - 10 = \underline{2}\ \underline{1}$

$42 - 10 = \underline{3}\ \underline{2}$

Circle the two numbers that make 10.
Add.

$\circled{8} + \circled{2} + 5 = 10 + \underline{\ 5\ }$
$= \underline{\ 15\ }$

$4 + 6 + 7 = 10 + \boxed{7}$
$= \underline{\quad}$

$2 + 3 + 7 = 10 + \underline{2}$
$= \underline{12}$

$1 + 6 + 4 = 10 + \underline{1}$
$= \underline{11}$

$8 + 5 + 5 = 10 + \underline{8}$
$= \underline{18}$

$7 + 6 + 3 = 10 + \underline{6}$
$= \underline{10}$

$4 + 9 + 1 = 10 + \underline{4}$
$= \underline{14}$

$8 + 3 + 2 = 10 + \underline{3}$
$= \underline{13}$

$4 + (5 + 5) = 10 + \underline{4}$
$= \underline{14}$

$\circled{2} + 9 + \circled{8} = 10 + \underline{9}$
$= \underline{19}$

$\circled{3} + 5 + \circled{7} = 10 + \underline{5}$
$= \underline{17}$

$\circled{1} + 8 + \circled{9} = 10 + \underline{8}$
$= \underline{18}$

188

# Hundreds Chart Pieces

The boxes are pieces from a hundreds chart.

| 1 | 2 | 3 | 4 | 5 | 6 | 7 | 8 | 9 | 10 |
|---|---|---|---|---|---|---|---|---|----|
| 11 | 12 | 13 | 14 | 15 | 16 | 17 | 18 | 19 | 20 |
| | | | | | | | | | |

☐ Find the missing numbers.

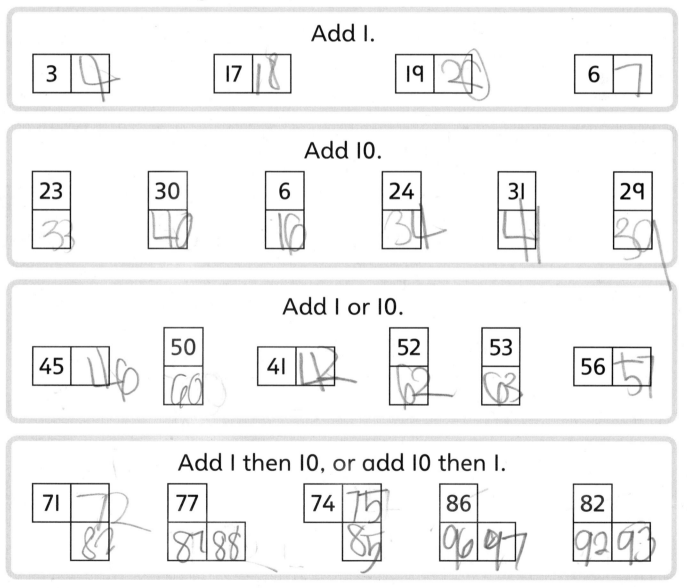

### Add 1.

| 3 | 4 |
|---|---|

| 17 | 18 |
|----|----|

| 19 | 20 |
|----|----|

| 6 | 7 |
|---|---|

### Add 10.

| 23 |
|----|
| 33 |

| 30 |
|----|
| 40 |

| 6 |
|---|
| 16 |

| 24 |
|----|
| 34 |

| 31 |
|----|
| 41 |

| 29 |
|----|
| 39 |

### Add 1 or 10.

45 | 46   50 / 60   41 | 42   52 / 62   53 / 63   56 | 57

### Add 1 then 10, or add 10 then 1.

71 | 72 / 81   77 / 87 88   74 | 75 / 85   86 / 96 97   82 / 92 93

☐ Have a partner check your answers using a hundreds chart.

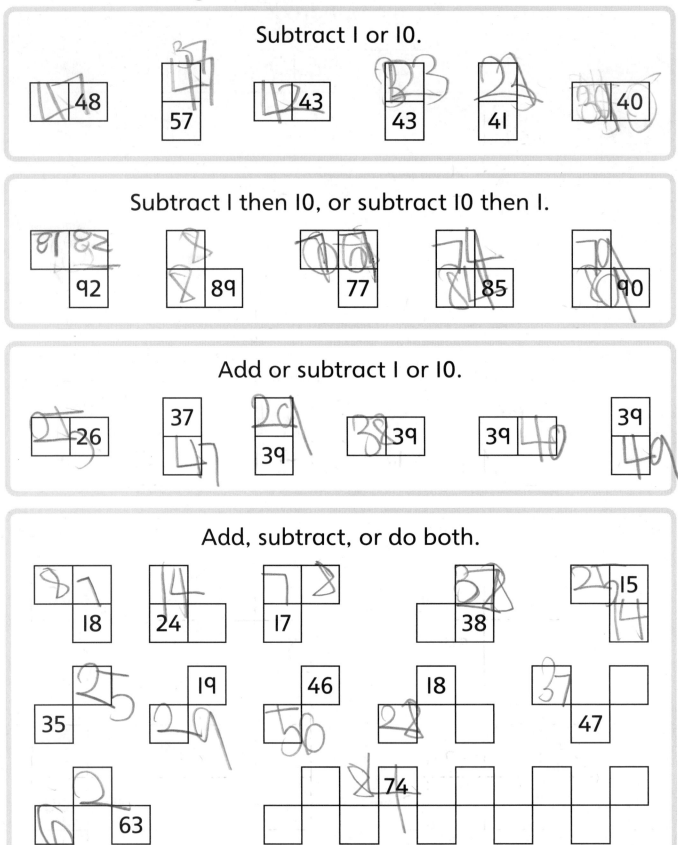

# Find the missing numbers.

**Subtract 1 or 10.**

| | 48 |
|---|---|

| | |
|---|---|
| | 57 |

| | 43 |
|---|---|

| | |
|---|---|
| | 43 |

| | |
|---|---|
| | 41 |

| | 40 |
|---|---|

**Subtract 1 then 10, or subtract 10 then 1.**

| | |
|---|---|
| 92 | |

| | |
|---|---|
| | 89 |

| | |
|---|---|
| | 77 |

| | |
|---|---|
| | 85 |

| | |
|---|---|
| | 90 |

**Add or subtract 1 or 10.**

| | 26 |
|---|---|

| 37 | |
|---|---|
| | |

| | |
|---|---|
| 39 | |

| | 39 |
|---|---|

| 39 | |
|---|---|

| 39 | |
|---|---|
| | |

**Add, subtract, or do both.**

| | |
|---|---|
| 18 | |

| | |
|---|---|
| 24 | |

| | |
|---|---|
| 17 | |

| | |
|---|---|
| | 38 |

| | 15 |
|---|---|
| | |

| | |
|---|---|
| 35 | |

| 19 | |
|---|---|
| | |

| 46 | |
|---|---|
| | |

| 18 | |
|---|---|
| | |

| | |
|---|---|
| | 47 |

| | |
|---|---|
| | 63 |

74

# Write the missing numbers on the hundreds chart pieces.

| 33 | 34 | 35 | 36 | 37 |
|----|----|----|----|----|
| 43 | 44 | 45 | 46 | 47 |
| 53 | 54 | 55 | 56 | 57 |

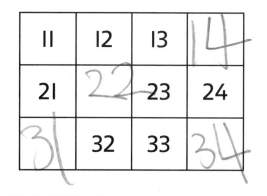

| 11 | 12 | 13 | 14 |
|----|----|----|----|
| 21 | 22 | 23 | 24 |
| 31 | 32 | 33 | 34 |

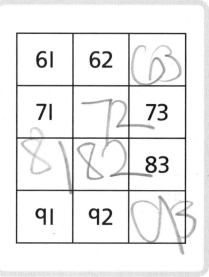

| 61 | 62 | 63 |
|----|----|----|
| 71 | 72 | 73 |
| 81 | 82 | 83 |
| 91 | 92 | 93 |

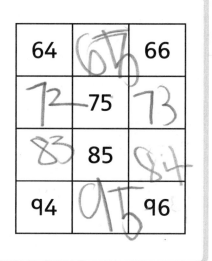

| 64 | 65 | 66 |
|----|----|----|
| 72 | 75 | 73 |
| 83 | 85 | 84 |
| 94 | 95 | 96 |

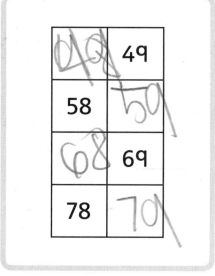

| 48 | 49 |
|----|----|
| 58 | 59 |
| 68 | 69 |
| 78 | 79 |

| 46 |    |    |    | 50 |
|----|----|----|----|----|
|    | 57 |    | 59 |    |
|    |    | 68 |    |    |
|    | 77 |    | 79 |    |
| 86 |    |    |    | 90 |

|    | 57 | 58 | 59 | 60 |
|----|----|----|----|----|
| 66 |    |    |    |    |
|    | 77 |    |    |    |
|    |    | 88 |    |    |
|    |    |    | 99 | 100 |

# Comparing Units of Length

☐ Measure two ways.
☐ Write which way needed more units and why.

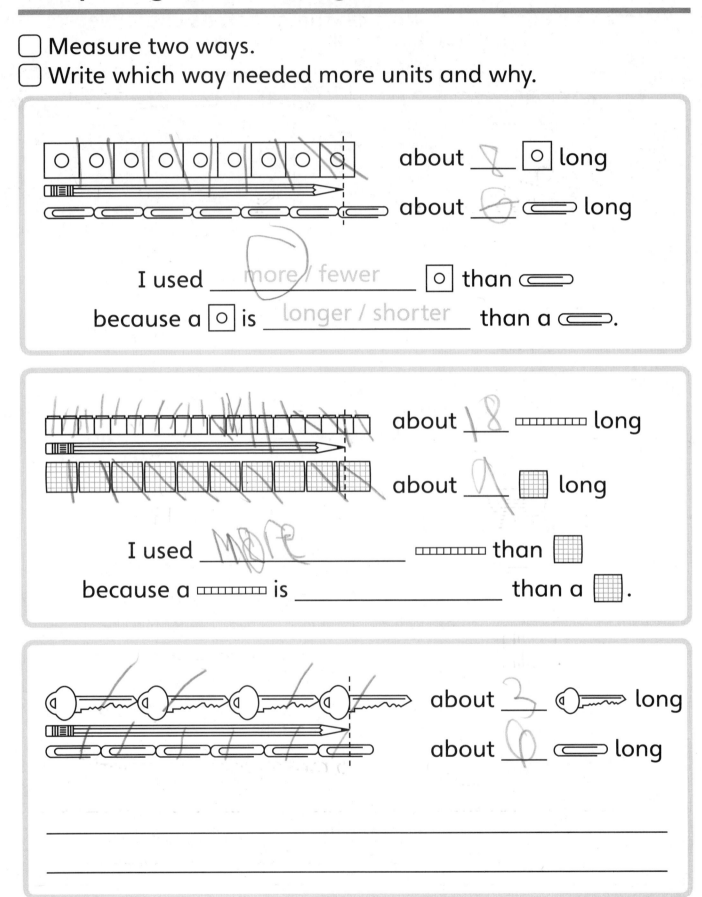

about __7__ ⬚ long

about __6__ ⬜ long

I used _____more / fewer_____ ⬚ than ⬜

because a ⬚ is _____longer / shorter_____ than a ⬜.

about __18__ ▭ long

about __9__ ▢ long

I used ___more___ ▭ than ▢

because a ▭ is _____ than a ▢.

about __3__ key long

about __6__ ⬜ long

_____

_____

# When You Do Not Have Many Units

☐ Measure a desk two ways.

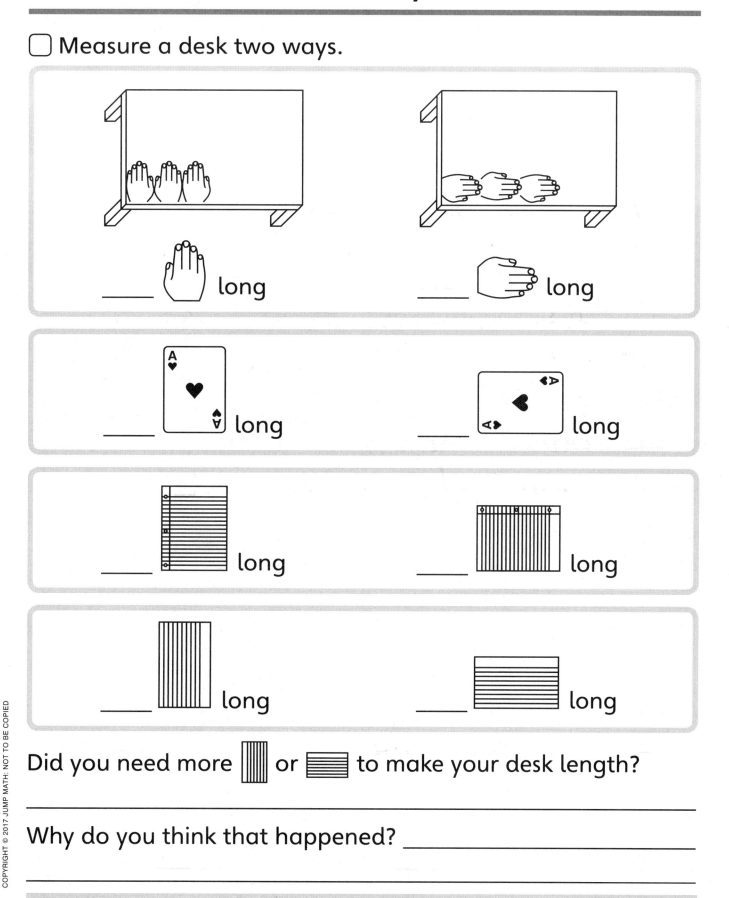

_____ 🖐 long          _____ 🤚 long

_____ 🂱 long          _____ 🃁 long

_____ 📄 long          _____ ▥ long

_____ ▥ long          _____ ▤ long

Did you need more ▥ or ▤ to make your desk length?

_____

Why do you think that happened? _____

_____

# Estimating

☐ Estimate how many small 🔲.
☐ Check by measuring.

Estimate: about __10__ small 🔲 long

Check: about __15__ small 🔲 long

Estimate: about _____ small 🔲 long

Check: about _____ small 🔲 long

Estimate: about _____ small 🔲 long

Check: about _____ small 🔲 long

Estimate: about _____ small 🔲 long

Check: about _____ small 🔲 long

☐ Use pictures to estimate.

☐ Use and to measure.

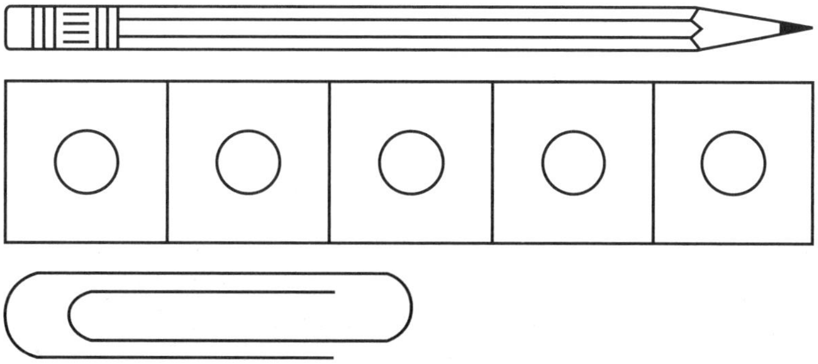

Estimate: _______ big long

Measure: _______ big long

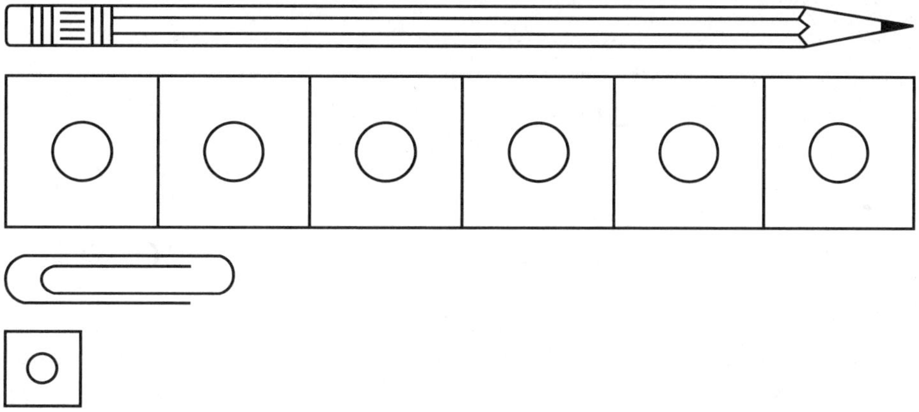

Estimate: _______ small long

Measure: _______ small long

Estimate: _______ small long

Measure: _______ small long

How did knowing the lengths in big help you estimate?

_______________________________________________

_______________________________________________

# Creating Rulers

☐ Make marks with equal spaces between them.
☐ Write the missing numbers on the ruler.

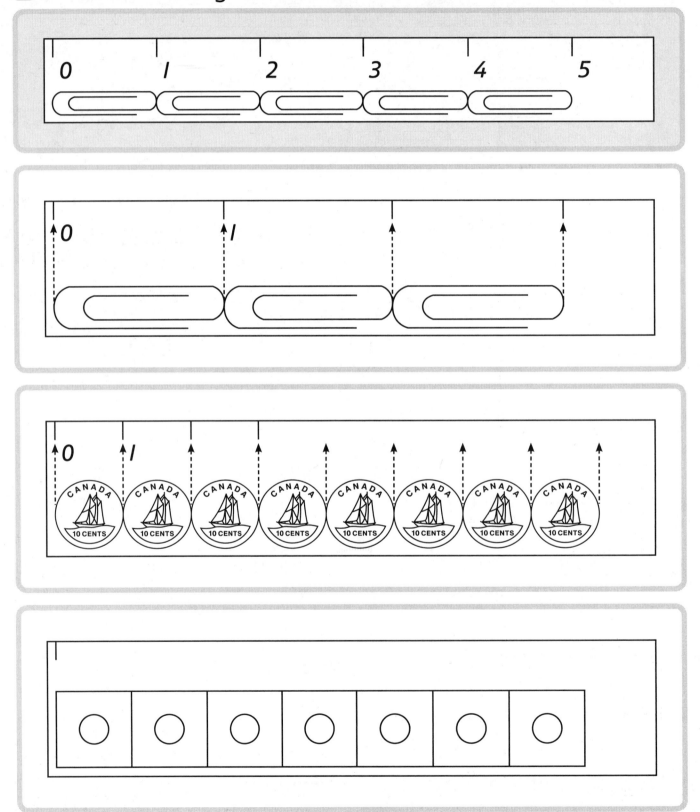

⬜ Write how many units long.

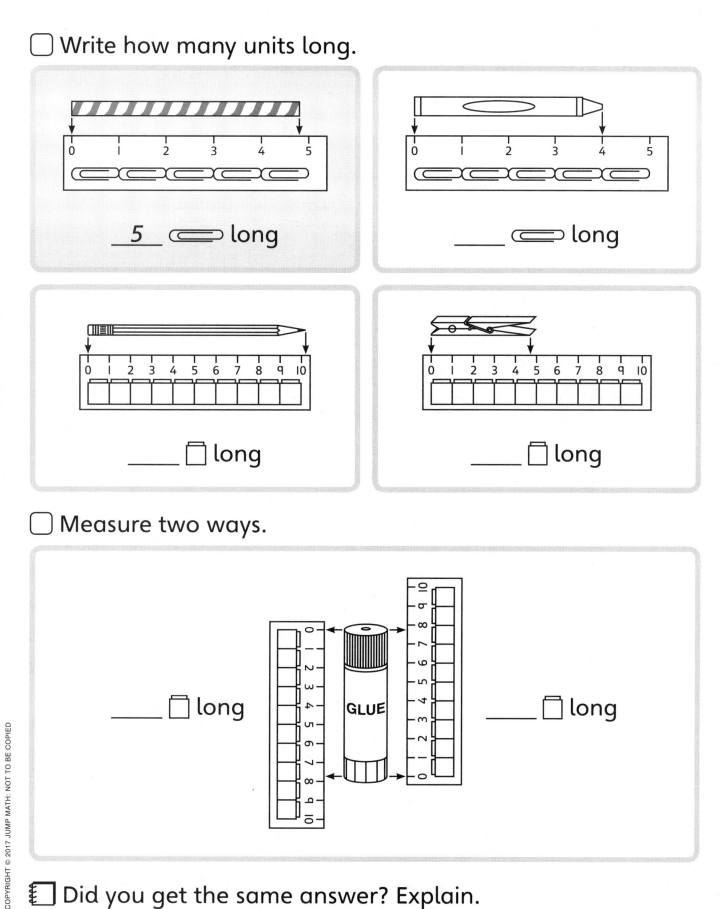

_5_ 🔗 long

_____ 🔗 long

_____ ☐ long

_____ ☐ long

⬜ Measure two ways.

_____ ☐ long

_____ ☐ long

▤ Did you get the same answer? Explain.

# Centimetres

A small 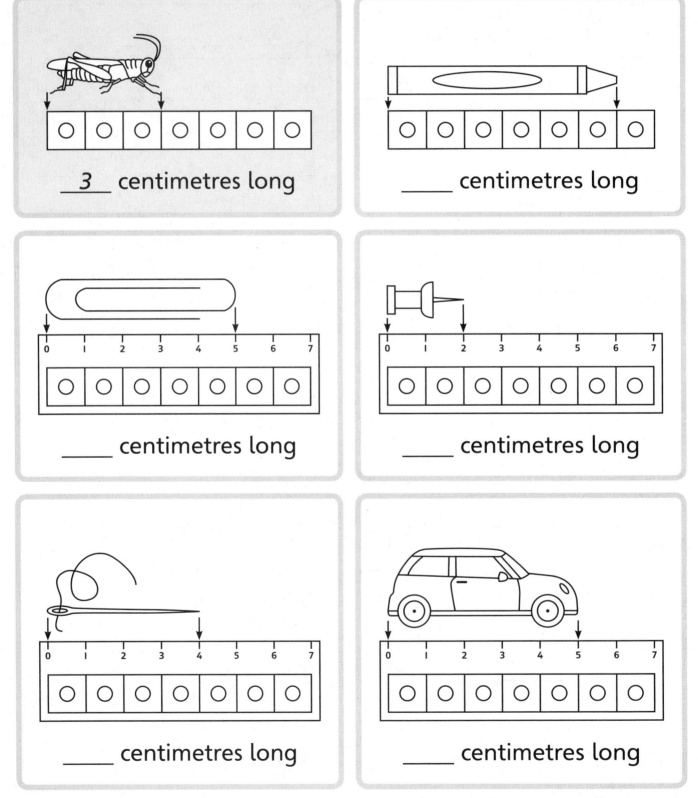 is I centimetre long.

☐ Write how many centimetres long.

_3_ centimetres long

____ centimetres long

____ centimetres long

____ centimetres long

____ centimetres long

____ centimetres long

# We write **cm** for **c**enti**m**etre.

☐ Fill in the blank.

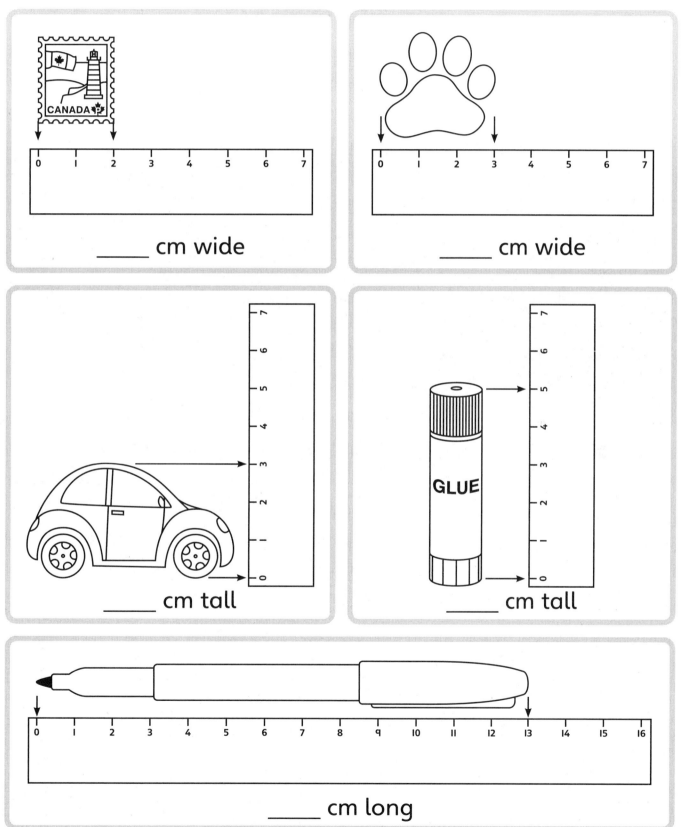

_____ cm wide

_____ cm wide

_____ cm tall

_____ cm tall

_____ cm long

☐ Measure the picture.

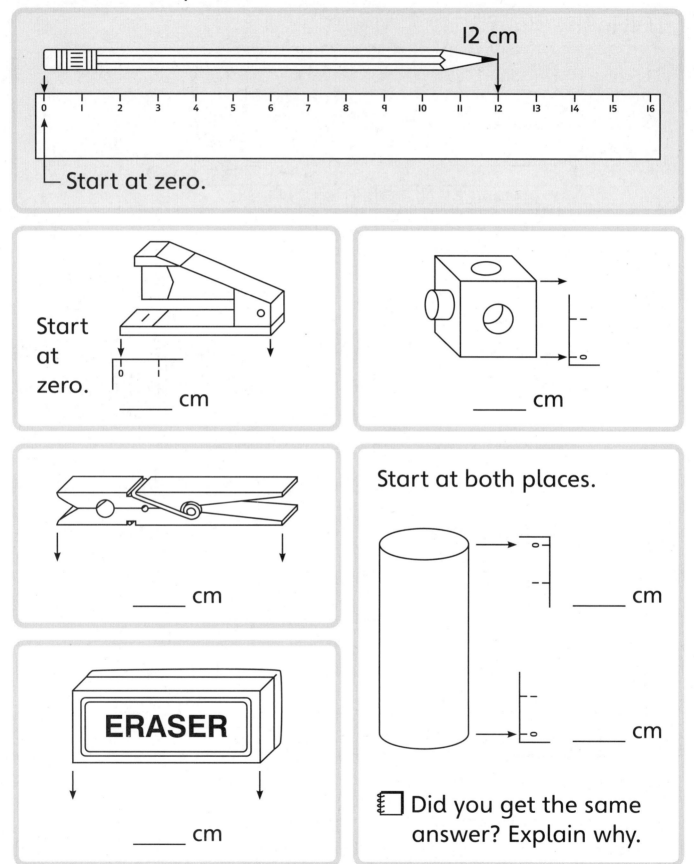

12 cm

0  1  2  3  4  5  6  7  8  9  10  11  12  13  14  15  16

Start at zero.

Start at zero.

_____ cm

_____ cm

_____ cm

Start at both places.

_____ cm

_____ cm

☐ Did you get the same answer? Explain why.

# Measuring Using Centimetre Grids

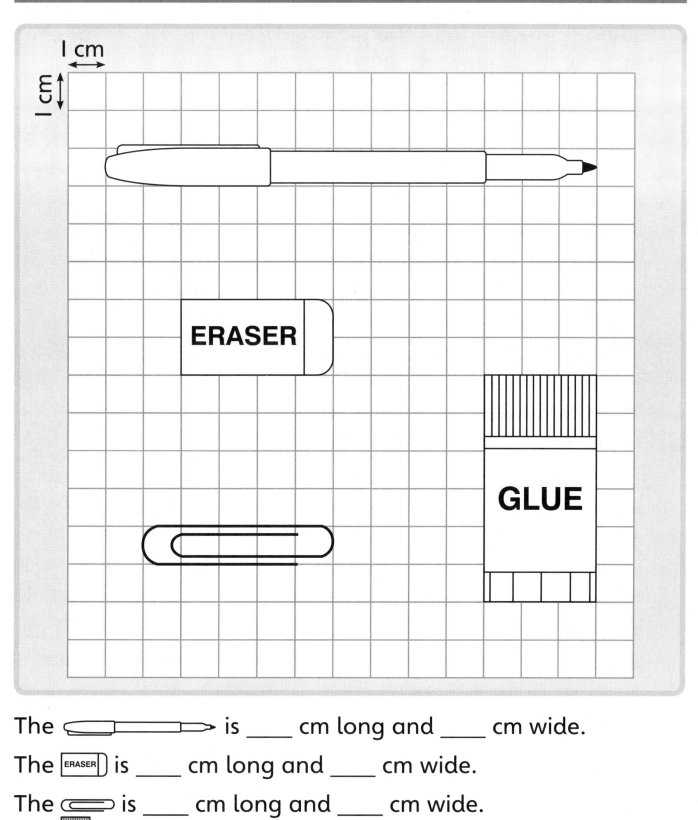

The ⟨pen⟩ is _____ cm long and _____ cm wide.

The ⟨ERASER⟩ is _____ cm long and _____ cm wide.

The ⟨paperclip⟩ is _____ cm long and _____ cm wide.

The ⟨GLUE⟩ is _____ cm tall and _____ cm wide.

# Estimating Centimetres

☐ Estimate the length of the picture. Use your fingers for cm.
☐ Measure the length in cm. Use a ruler.

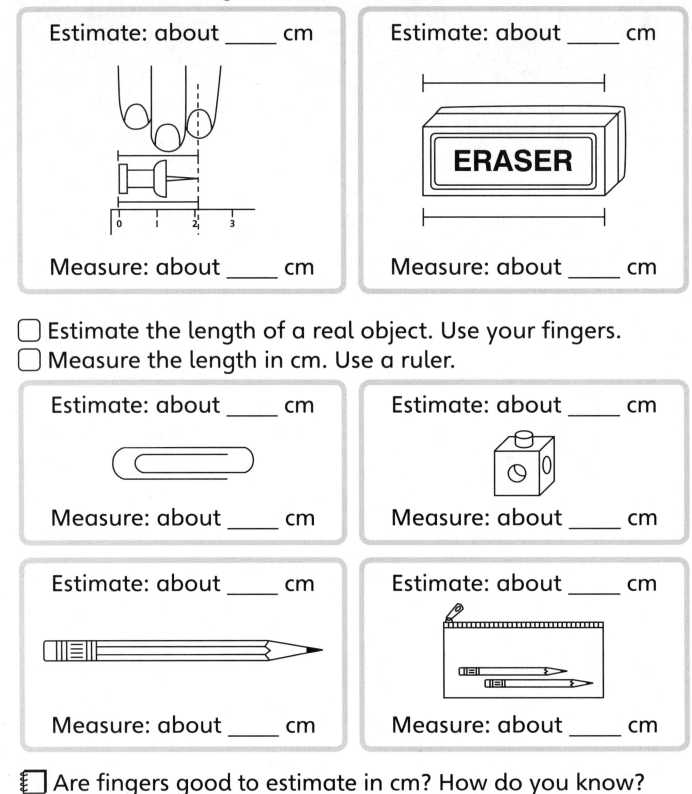

Estimate: about _____ cm

Measure: about _____ cm

Estimate: about _____ cm

Measure: about _____ cm

☐ Estimate the length of a real object. Use your fingers.
☐ Measure the length in cm. Use a ruler.

Estimate: about _____ cm

Measure: about _____ cm

Estimate: about _____ cm

Measure: about _____ cm

Estimate: about _____ cm

Measure: about _____ cm

Estimate: about _____ cm

Measure: about _____ cm

☐ Are fingers good to estimate in cm? How do you know?

# Metres

Here is how to measure with only one metre stick.

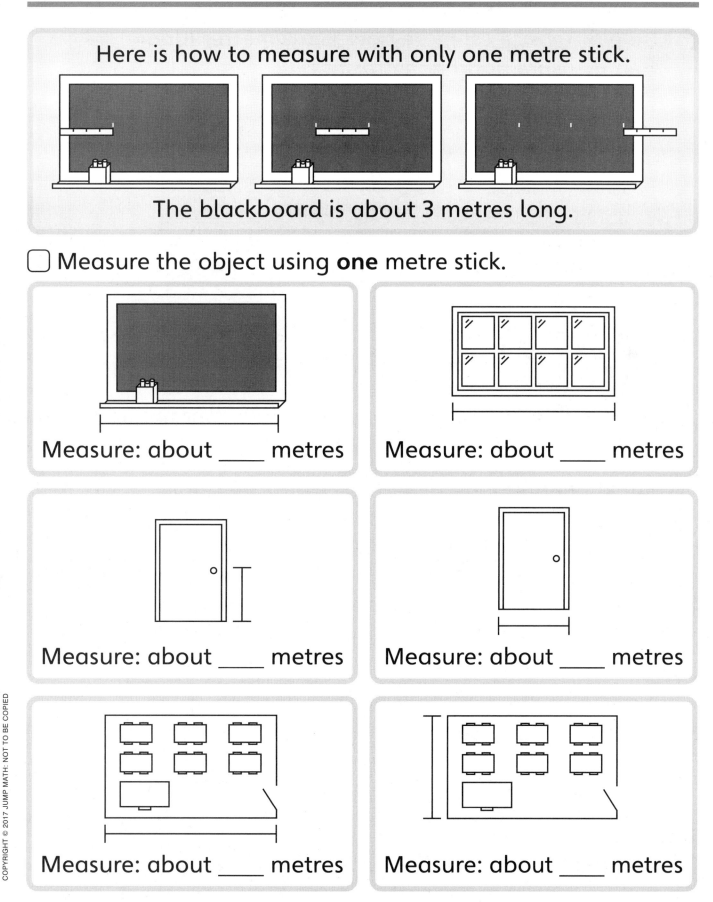

The blackboard is about 3 metres long.

☐ Measure the object using **one** metre stick.

Measure: about _____ metres

Measure: about _____ metres

Measure: about _____ metres

Measure: about _____ metres

Measure: about _____ metres

Measure: about _____ metres

# Estimating Metres

☐ Use big steps to estimate how many metres long.
☐ Then measure using a metre stick.

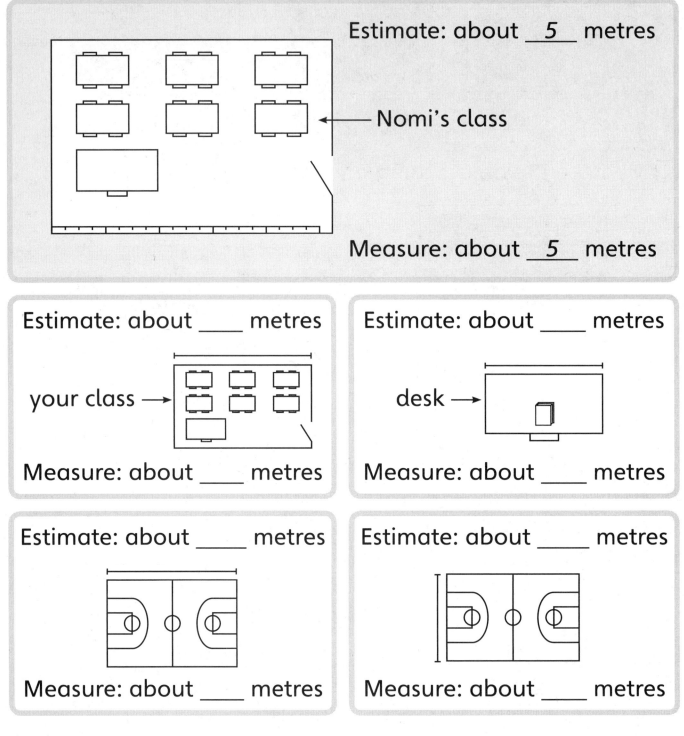

Estimate: about __5__ metres

Nomi's class

Measure: about __5__ metres

Estimate: about ____ metres

your class →

Measure: about ____ metres

Estimate: about ____ metres

desk →

Measure: about ____ metres

Estimate: about ____ metres

Measure: about ____ metres

Estimate: about ____ metres

Measure: about ____ metres

## Bonus

How can you estimate the **height** of your classroom in metres?

# Would you use **m** or **cm** to measure the object? Why?

a tree: *m*
because *trees are very tall*

a swimming pool: ____
because _____

a clothespin: ____
because _____

a bottle: ____
because _____

around the park: ____
because _____

a spoon: ____
because _____

your school: ____
because _____

around your wrist: ____
because _____

# Comparing Masses

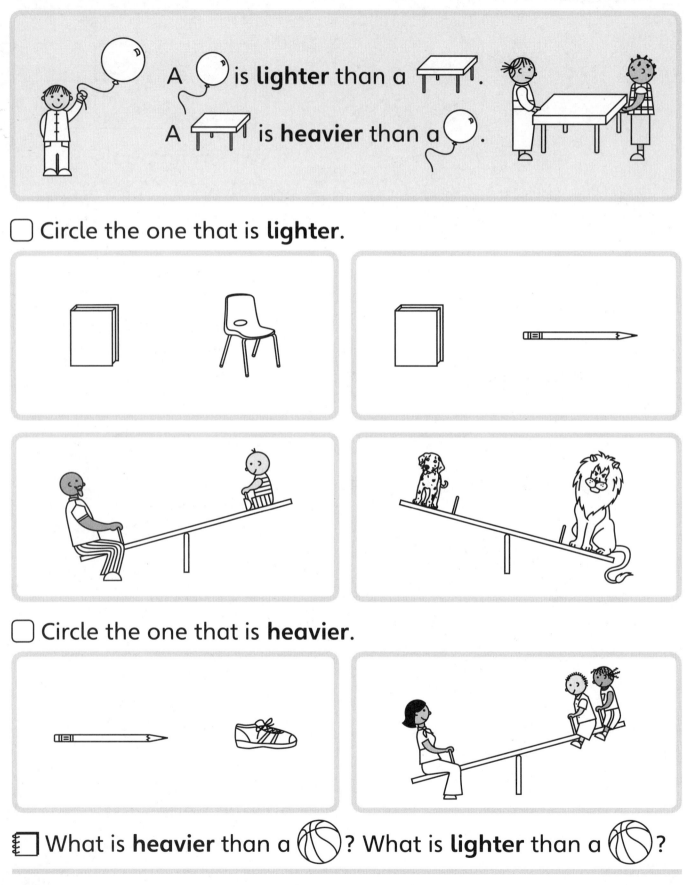

A 🎈 is **lighter** than a 🪑.

A 🪑 is **heavier** than a 🎈.

☐ Circle the one that is **lighter**.

☐ Circle the one that is **heavier**.

📓 What is **heavier** than a 🏀? What is **lighter** than a 🏀?

☐ Draw the balance.

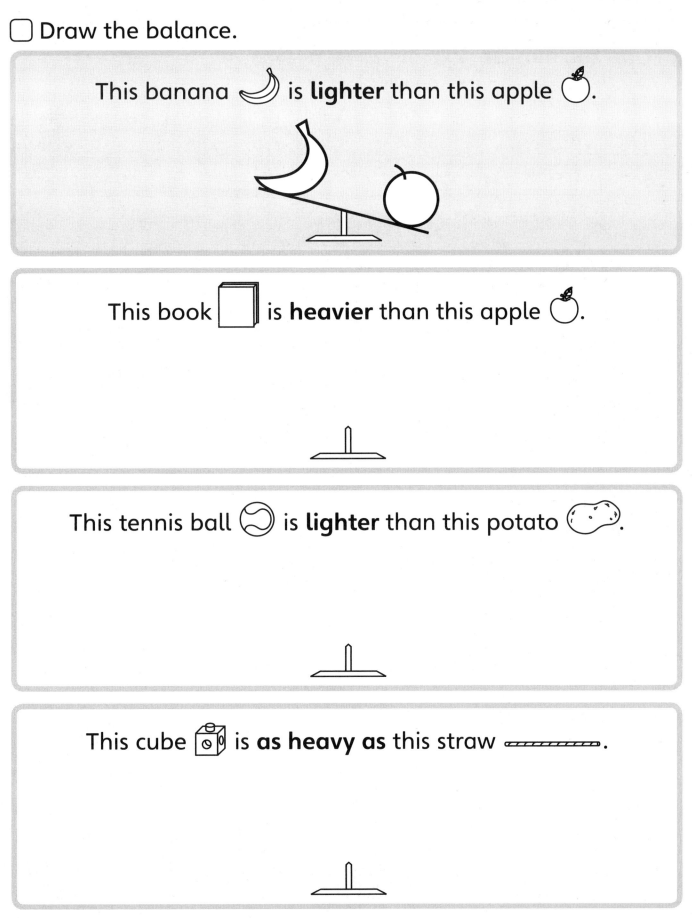

This banana is **lighter** than this apple.

This book is **heavier** than this apple.

This tennis ball is **lighter** than this potato.

This cube is **as heavy as** this straw.

# Measuring Mass

☐ Find the mass in 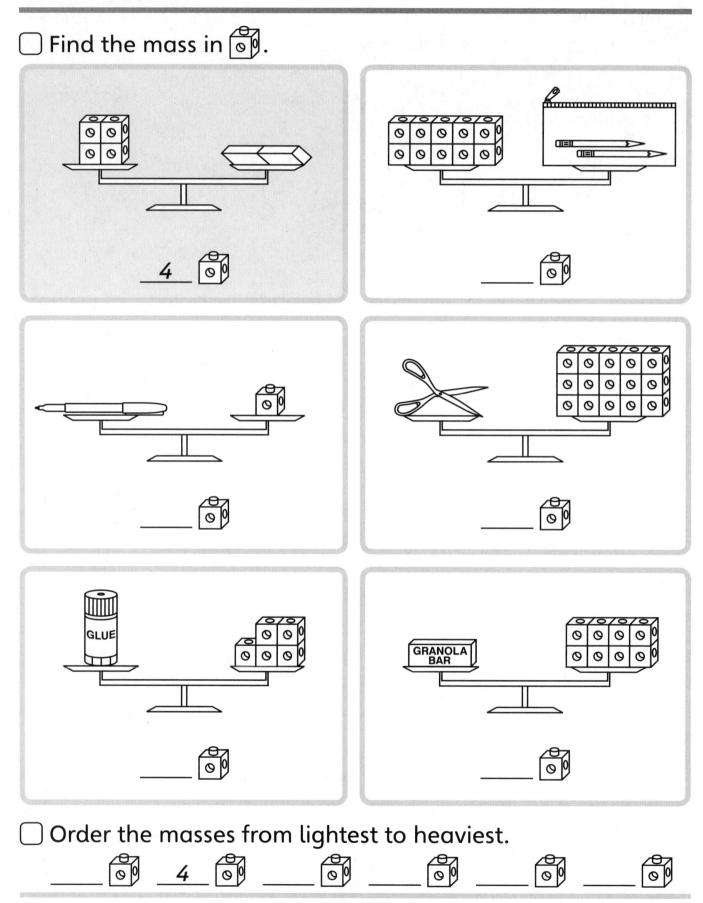.

4

____ ____ ____ ____ ____

GLUE

GRANOLA BAR

☐ Order the masses from lightest to heaviest.

____   4   ____   ____   ____   ____   ____

# Which is **heavier?**

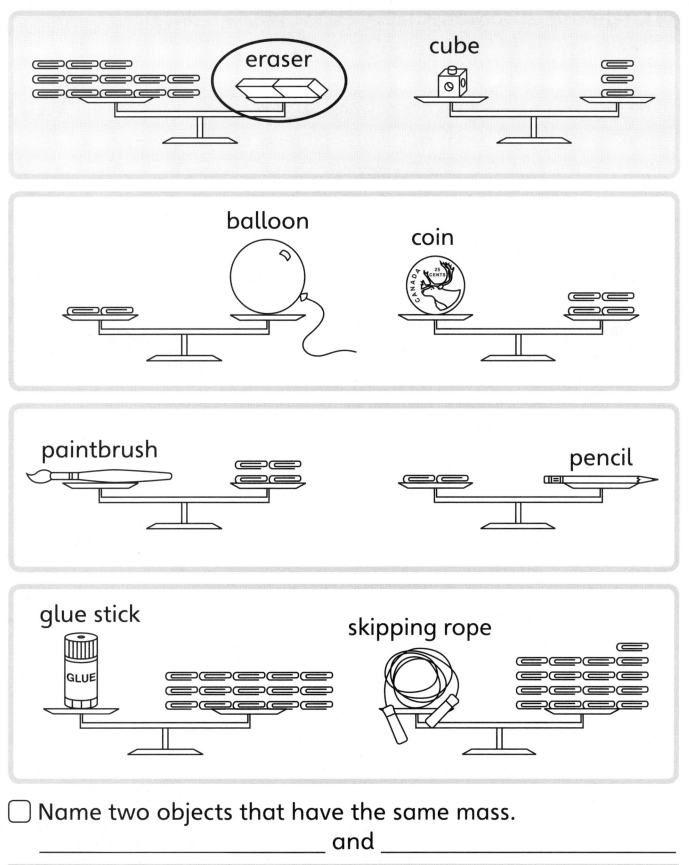

☐ Name two objects that have the same mass.

_____ and _____

# Which picture is more balanced?
☐ Circle the closer mass.

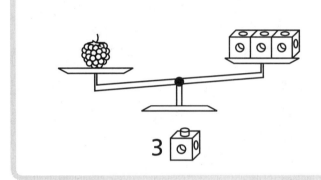
3 🎲

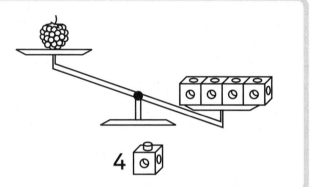
4 🎲

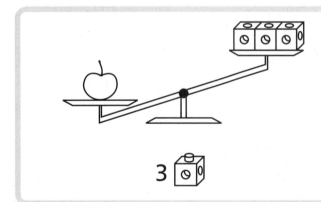
3 🎲

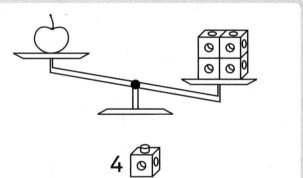
4 🎲

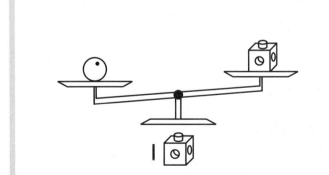
1 🎲

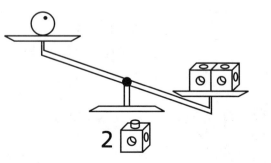
2 🎲

**Measurement 2-18**

# Estimating and Measuring Mass

☐ Estimate. Is the mass closer to 10 large 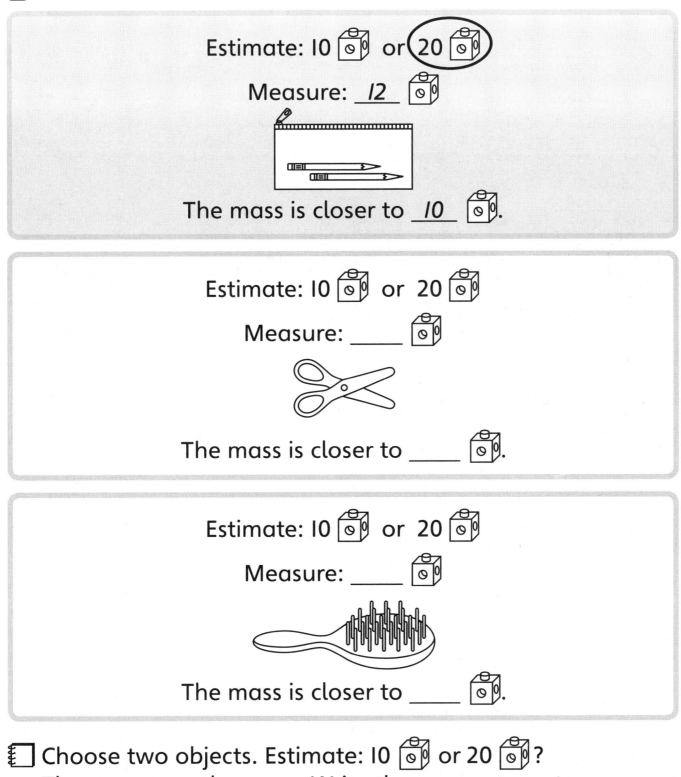 or 20 large ? <br>
☐ Measure.

Estimate: 10  or ⟨20⟩

Measure: _12_

The mass is closer to _10_ .

Estimate: 10  or  20

Measure: ____

The mass is closer to ____ .

Estimate: 10  or  20

Measure: ____

The mass is closer to ____ .

⌸ Choose two objects. Estimate: 10  or 20 ? <br>
Then measure the mass. Write the measurement.

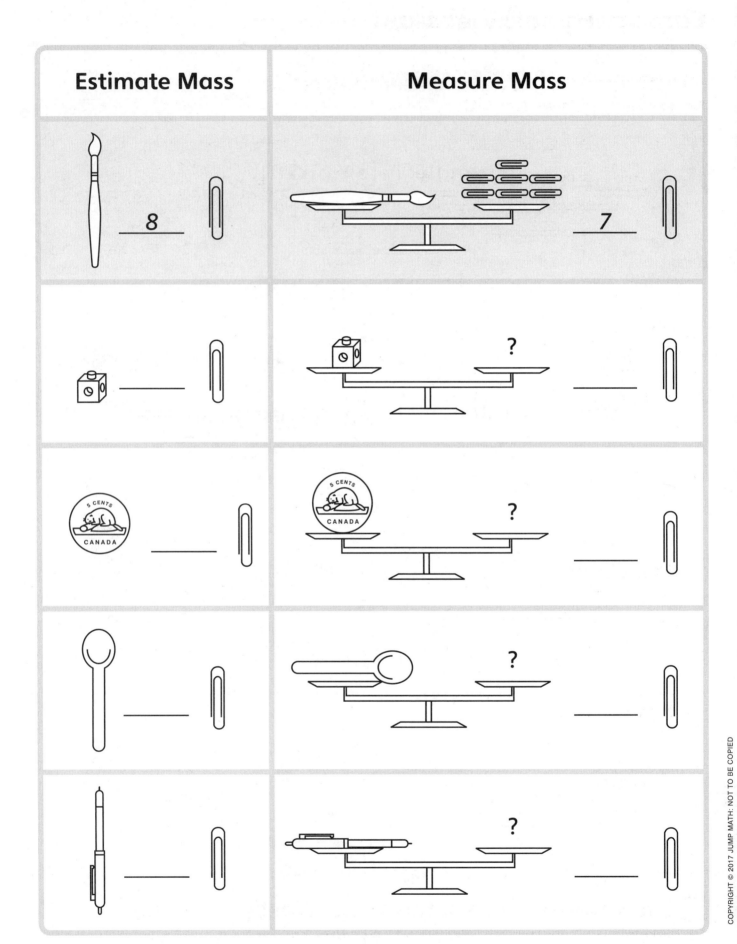

# Estimate Mass

# Measure Mass

8 ___ <br> 7 ___

# Comparing Units of Mass

☐ Measure with big ▭ and big ⬚.

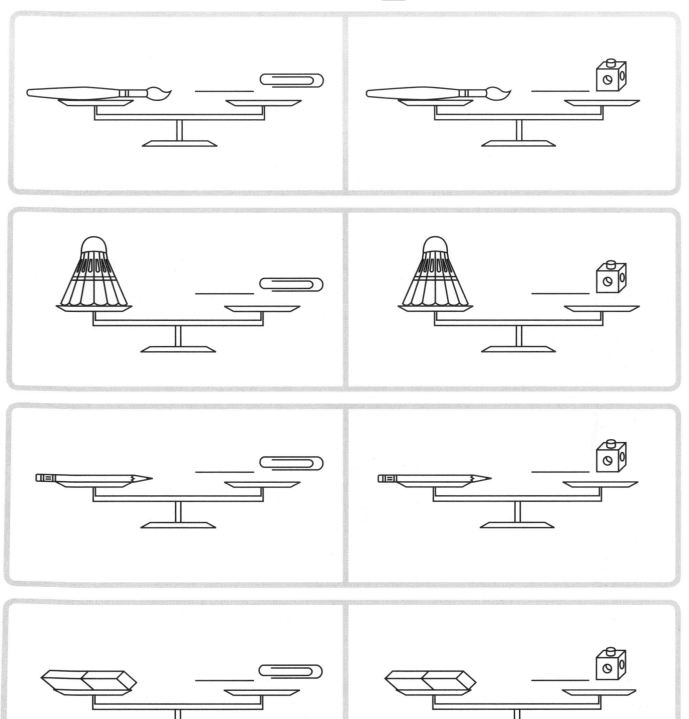

📓 Did you need more ▭ or ⬚? Why?

# What is the mass of the apple?

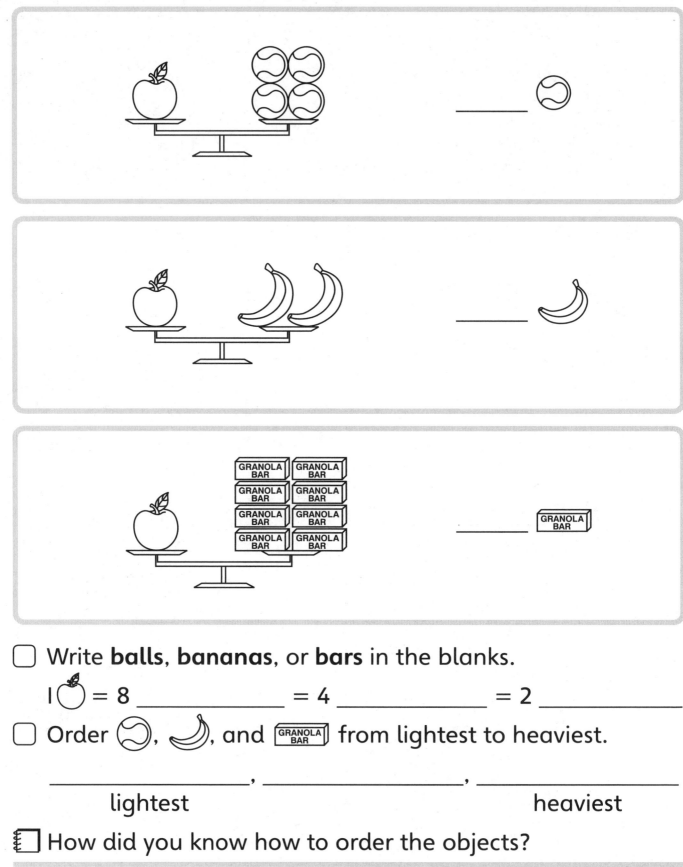

☐ Write **balls**, **bananas**, or **bars** in the blanks.

1 🍎 = 8 _____ = 4 _____ = 2 _____

☐ Order ⊙, 🍌, and 〔GRANOLA BAR〕 from lightest to heaviest.

_____ , _____ , _____

      lightest                                       heaviest

📓 How did you know how to order the objects?